American Speak Out

Upper-Intermediate Workbook

Frances Eales • Steve Oakes
• Louis Harrison

CONTENTS

1 NEW THINGS — Page 4

1.1
- READING | Speed Shrinking
- VOCABULARY | personality
- GRAMMAR | direct and indirect questions
- WRITING | an advice forum message; learn to edit for accuracy

1.2
- VOCABULARY | feelings
- LISTENING | Dreams Come True
- GRAMMAR | present perfect
- VOCABULARY PLUS | word building: nouns

1.3
- VOCABULARY | ads
- FUNCTION | polite inquiries
- LEARN TO | manage inquiries

2 ISSUES — Page 9

2.1
- VOCABULARY | issues
- GRAMMAR | present perfect simple and continuous
- LISTENING | We Are What We Do
- VOCABULARY PLUS | verbs/nouns with the same form

2.2
- READING | So you want to be a spy?
- VOCABULARY | surveillance
- GRAMMAR | the passive
- WRITING | a letter of complaint; learn to use formal written language

2.3
- FUNCTION | opinions
- LEARN TO | support your viewpoint
- VOCABULARY | opinion adjectives

Review 1 — Page 14

3 STORIES — Page 18

3.1
- GRAMMAR | narrative tenses
- LISTENING | The Seven Types of Stories
- VOCABULARY | sayings
- WRITING | a story

3.2
- VOCABULARY | adjectives for stories
- GRAMMAR | I wish, If only
- READING | Outstanding
- VOCABULARY PLUS | multi-word verbs

3.3
- VOCABULARY | reading genres
- FUNCTION | expressing likes and dislikes
- LEARN TO | summarize a plot

4 DOWNTIME — Page 23

4.1
- LISTENING | Are you addicted to social networking?
- VOCABULARY | free time
- GRAMMAR | present and past habits
- WRITING | an opinion essay; learn to use linkers

4.2
- READING | Space tourism is here!
- VOCABULARY | positive adjectives
- GRAMMAR | future forms
- VOCABULARY PLUS | uncountable and plural nouns

4.3
- FUNCTION | describing procedures
- VOCABULARY | abilities
- LEARN TO | use mirror questions

Review 2 — Page 28

5 IDEAS — Page 32

5.1
- LISTENING | The Ig Nobel Prize
- VOCABULARY | change
- GRAMMAR | articles
- VOCABULARY PLUS | compound nouns

5.2
- READING | The Ten Best and Worst Words in Advertising
- VOCABULARY | advertising collocations
- GRAMMAR | real and hypothetical conditionals
- WRITING | a report; learn to make written comparisons

5.3
- FUNCTION | suggesting ideas
- VOCABULARY | collocations with *idea*
- LEARN TO | show reservations

6 AGE — Page 37

6.1
- VOCABULARY | age
- GRAMMAR | modal verbs and related phrases
- LISTENING | What's the best age … ?
- VOCABULARY PLUS | word-building: prefixes

6.2
- READING | 2030 Vision
- GRAMMAR | future perfect and continuous
- VOCABULARY | optimism/pessimism
- WRITING | an informal email; learn to focus on informal style

6.3
- VOCABULARY | collocations
- FUNCTION | persuading
- LEARN TO | clarify ideas

Review 3 — Page 42

CONTENTS

7 MEDIA — Page 46

- **7.1** VOCABULARY | television
  GRAMMAR | quantifiers
  LISTENING | favorite childhood TV program
  VOCABULARY PLUS | multi-word verbs
- **7.2** READING | Say "Cheese" Now … Sue Later
  GRAMMAR | reported speech
  VOCABULARY | reporting verbs
  WRITING | a discursive essay; learn to use linkers of contrast
- **7.3** VOCABULARY | the press
  FUNCTION | adding emphasis
  LEARN TO | make guesses

8 BEHAVIOR — Page 51

- **8.1** VOCABULARY | collocations: decisions
  VOCABULARY PLUS | compound adjectives
  LISTENING | behavior experiment
  GRAMMAR | past and mixed conditionals
- **8.2** READING | Sleep Positions Give Clue to the Nation's Personality
  VOCABULARY | values
  GRAMMAR | -ing form and infinitive
  WRITING | an informal article; learn how to use linkers of purpose
- **8.3** VOCABULARY | behavior
  FUNCTION | handling an awkward situation
  LEARN TO | soften a message

Review 4 — Page 56

9 TROUBLE — Page 60

- **9.1** LISTENING | inattentional blindness
  GRAMMAR | -ing form and infinitive
  VOCABULARY | crime
  VOCABULARY PLUS | dependent prepositions
- **9.2** READING | Five Reasons You'll Fall for an Internet Scam
  VOCABULARY | synonyms
  GRAMMAR | past modals of deduction
  WRITING | a "how to" leaflet; learn to avoid repetition
- **9.3** FUNCTION | reporting an incident
  VOCABULARY | incidents
  LEARN TO | rephrase

10 CULTURE — Page 65

- **10.1** READING | Movie Fan Forum
  VOCABULARY | adjectives to describe movies
  GRAMMAR | relative clauses
  WRITING | a review; learn to use adverb + past participle combinations
- **10.2** GRAMMAR | participle clauses
  VOCABULARY | the arts
  LISTENING | how to take a good picture
  VOCABULARY PLUS | two-part phrases
- **10.3** FUNCTION | giving a tour
  VOCABULARY | dimensions
  LEARN TO | express estimates

Review 5 — Page 70

AUDIO SCRIPTS — Page 74

READING

FIRST THERE WAS **SPEED DATING**
THEN **SPEED ROOMMATING** ... AND NOW ...

SPEED SHRINKING:
A THREE-MINUTE CURE?

1 New Yorkers are famous for spending more time with their therapists, or "shrinks," than with their friends. Whether that's true is open to debate, but with the arrival of speed shrinking, they'll find they have more time left for their personal life and more cash left in their pockets as well.

2 "You only have three minutes to say your problem and get advice," said Andu Novac, the first person I spoke to when I arrived at my first speed-shrinking event. "That's so you don't waste time going into detail."

3 In the newest variant of a format that seems to be inspired by speed dating, participants have the opportunity to seek the advice of eight different therapists, each providing a three-minute session. Speed shrinking is the brainchild of Susan Shapiro, a professor of journalism who has also written a book on the subject. Shapiro stumbled across the idea a few years ago when she herself was looking for a new therapist and found a way to try out several of them at minimal cost.

4 This evening's event, held in a college lecture hall, is free and has attracted a long line of people hoping to find a quick cure for their emotional quandaries. Many of those attending are unwilling to talk about their worries to anyone but the therapists, but problems seem to run the gamut from broken relationships, to anxiety about work and money, to general depression, as well as a variety of phobias. Advice tends to be succinct and practical, as suits the format.

5 "I'm really unhappy in my job," Novac tells therapist Adrian Jones. "I wish I'd become a painter, but now I feel stuck in this position I have at a bank." "Follow your dreams," Jones tells him. "You may end up poorer, but you won't have the regret of not doing what you really want to do." Jones's advice hardly seems original, but Novac says he is satisfied. "I liked his style—he seemed to understand and care," explains Novac. "I'm actually looking for a new therapist and this is a great way to try out eight of them in a short time."

6 That's actually why many therapists take part in the event, Jones tells us. "This is a great source of new clients. And it's a good way for me to advertise my new book—I just have it on the table in front of me and refer to it during my sessions."

7 Some of those seeking advice aren't entirely happy with the format. "People near me can hear what I'm telling the therapist," remarks Donna Bersch. "I feel self-conscious." But with the loud buzz in the room that sometimes reaches the level of shouting, it's hard to imagine that anyone could actually eavesdrop on another session. Sometimes, they're lucky to be able to hear the person sitting across from them!

Roommating / college
line / check / organized

Flatmating / university
queue / tick / organised

1 A Read the heading and check (✓) the best summary, a), b) or c). Then read the article and check.

a) It's about a service where overweight people can lose weight quickly.
b) It's about a service where people can get advice from a therapist in a short time.
c) It's about a service where people get help making their lives simpler.

B Match the people 1–4 with the roles a)–c).

1 Novac   *b*   a) therapist
2 Shapiro   b) client
3 Jones   c) founder
4 Bersch

C Are the statements true (T) or false (F)? Underline the words/phrases in the article that helped you.

1 New Yorkers prefer to spend more time with their therapists than with their friends.   F
2 Shapiro works at a college.
3 In speed shrinking, the therapist gets paid cash.
4 A lot of people don't want to tell the reporter what their problems are.
5 Novac thinks that Jones's advice is disappointingly unoriginal.
6 Many of the therapists participate in order to get more business.
7 Bersch doesn't like how noisy it gets sometimes.
8 People sometimes can't hear each other because they talk too softly.

D Find words in the article to match definitions 1–8.

1 the way that something is organized or designed (paragraph 3)
   format

2 idea or plan that one person has thought of (paragraph 3)
   _____

3 found by chance (paragraph 3)
   _____

4 difficult situations where you cannot decide what to do (paragraph 4)
   _____

5 strong unreasonable fears of particular things (paragraph 4)
   _____

6 clearly expressed in a few words (paragraph 4)
   _____

7 a job in a particular organization (paragraph 5)
   _____

8 secretly listen to another person's conversation (paragraph 7)
   _____

VOCABULARY
PERSONALITY

2 A Correct the mistake in each phrase.

                             to

1 I don't know why you say he's down-on-earth, *c*
2 I never plan what I say, I'm very spontaneously,
3 Fabio tends to keep in himself. I don't see much of him because
4 My colleague Bill is a real person person,

a) and other people seem to think I'm quick and wit because of that.
b) you can tell he enjoys company because he's such a good laughter.
c) I think he's a real computer gawk, and he's not very practical.
d) he arrives at work early and leaves early—he's a morn person, and I'm not.

B Match the sentence halves.

GRAMMAR
DIRECT AND INDIRECT QUESTIONS

3 Make the therapist's questions with the prompts.

1 Why / you / come / see / me / today?
   A: *Why have you come to see me today?*
   B: I keep getting headaches.

2 What / these headaches / like?
   A: _____
   B: Absolutely terrible.

3 What / cause / the headaches, / think?
   A: _____
   B: Mainly thinking about money.

4 What / think / about / moment?
   A: _____
   B: That clock.

5 that clock / remind / you / anything?
   A: _____
   B: Yes, money.

6 Why / that?
   A: _____
   B: Because I'm paying by the minute! Let's stop now.

7 OK. / How / like / pay— / cash / credit card?
   A: _____

4 A Complete the second sentence so that it has a similar meaning to the first. Use between two and five words, including the word given.

1 Could you introduce us to the director? WONDER
   I *wonder if you could introduce* us to the director.

2 How much did your camera cost? CAMERA
   Do you mind me _____ cost?

3 What do you do exactly? TELLING
   Would you mind _____ do exactly?

4 Is it really worth upgrading to the new smartphone? WHETHER
   I'd like to know _____ worth upgrading to the new smartphone.

5 Which platform does the Eurostar train leave from? TRAIN
   Can you tell me which platform _____ from?

6 What will he do when he discovers the mistake? DO
   What do you _____ when he discovers the mistake?

B Listen and check. Then listen and repeat, paying attention to the polite intonation.

WRITING
AN ADVICE FORUM MESSAGE; LEARN TO EDIT FOR ACCURACY

5 A Read the forum question and reply below. Use the correction code to mark the mistakes and then correct them.

Correction Code:	sp = spelling
v = verb form	p = punctuation
gr = grammar	wo = word order
ww = wrong word	st = style

JUSTINE

Can anyone helping ¹_____? I've just received my essay to write about personality, but the articles I've found are too difficult for me to read. Then I realised the real problem is my poor vocabulary. When I reed ²_____ quickly, I can't understand the real meaning of the article, and the only way I can understand it is by using my dictionary all the time. I'm reading so slowly it's going to take me about three weeks to finish the writing ³_____.
What can I do about my English vocabulary? I'm worried so ⁴_____.

MARTA

Justine, keep calm? ⁵_____ I know what you mean. The first time I wrote an essay in a foreign language, reading was the most difficult thing, and the most difficult part of reading was vocabulary. The first thing to do is discuss the problem with your teacher. The next thing is to obtain ⁶_____ a good English–English dictionary. I joined a language-learning community. I joined the group ⁷_____ with a similar problem, and we all helped each other with our vocabulary. Try it!

B Write a reply from Justine to Marta (120–150 words). Thank her for her suggestions, say which you think are most useful, which you will try and what other ways of learning vocabulary you are going to try.

1.2

VOCABULARY
FEELINGS

1 A Put the letters in the correct order to make words and phrases. The first letter of each word is underlined.

1 (made my) amcu<u>t</u>h<u>s</u>notr _____stomach turn_____
2 n<u>o</u>pt<u>o</u>f<u>o</u>htldroe<u>w</u> _____
3 niga<u>s</u>kh (like a leaf) _____
4 (wish the ground would) all<u>s</u>wem<u>o</u>uwp _____
5 d<u>a</u>rka<u>w</u>w _____
6 li<u>v</u>edeer _____
7 <u>s</u>af<u>o</u>teud<u>o</u>rc (my wits) _____
8 gnica<u>f</u>satin _____
9 r<u>a</u>dtsfruet _____
10 seedpr<u>i</u>sm _____

B Complete the sentences with the correct form of the words and phrases from Exercise 1A.

1 My audition was terrible, I was so anxious I was _____.
2 You look totally disgusted. You look like your _____. They're only oysters!
3 I find volcanoes really _____. I've read lots of books on the topic.
4 I lost my place in the middle of giving the presentation. It was really embarrassing—I just wished the _____ me up.
5 We went to Cairo to see the exhibition, but it was closed. I was really _____!
6 My wife came into the store when I was buying her some perfume. It was pretty _____, and I had to hide what I was doing.
7 Seiji had been missing for hours, so his parents were enormously _____ when they found him safe and sound.
8 When the plane started bumping up and down, I was _____. I was really frightened. I thought we were going to die.
9 You have a great singing voice. I'm really _____.
10 I was pretty worried about the test yesterday. I thought I'd failed it, so I was _____ to find out that I'd gotten a good grade.

C Which of the sentences in Exercise 1B contain modifiers (*pretty*, *totally*, etc.) that can be replaced by *very*?

LISTENING

2 A Read the ad and listen to the interview. Number the pictures A–C in the order the dreams are mentioned.

A ☐   B ☐   C ☐

DREAMS COME TRUE

Do you have experiences you've always wanted to have but never thought were possible?

Whether your dream is ordinary or extraordinary, it's special to us!

With Dreams Come True, there's always a first time—we guarantee it!

B Listen again and circle the correct answer.

1 What did the first client want?
  a) to appear with a rock star in a live concert
  b) people to recognize her talent
  c) to play in front of a large number of people
2 Why does Owen Winters find his job at Dreams Come True easy?
  a) It's similar to his previous job.
  b) He has worked in business for many years.
  c) He knows a lot of people in the music business.
3 What is the secret about the supersonic flight?
  a) the name of the client who wants to fly
  b) the financial details of the flight
  c) where the plane comes from
4 How did the person with Tom Cruise make-up feel about the experience?
  a) He loved all the attention.
  b) He didn't enjoy it.
  c) He didn't like the bodyguards.
5 What happened to the woman who wanted to go into space?
  a) She couldn't afford it at first, but now she can.
  b) She was originally disappointed, but now she's going to achieve her dream.
  c) It has taken Dreams Come True a long time to plan and organize the trip.

C Listen again. How many of the dreams mentioned are connected with pop culture (P), transportation (T) or history (H)?

---

the ground would swallow me up
store / pretty / recognize

the earth would swallow me up
shop / quite / recognise

GRAMMAR
PRESENT PERFECT

3 Complete the sentences with the present perfect or past simple form of the verbs in parentheses.

1 Is there something you _have always wanted_ (always want) to do but somehow _____ (never manage) to?

2 Not long ago our company _____ (have) a client who _____ (want) to be a rock star.

3 I _____ (work) as a production manager in the movie business for many years, till just a few years ago.

4 How much _____ (the concert / cost) last year? _____ (the cost / go) up since then?

5 What other dreams _____ (you / make) come true recently?

6 We _____ (just finish) working with a client who wants to fly across the Atlantic Ocean on a supersonic airplane.

7 One client wanted to fly in space, but that wasn't possible back when she first _____ (request) it.

8 Since then it _____ (become) possible for ordinary people to go into space.

4 Complete the conversations with the present perfect or past simple form of the verbs in the box.

> speak   forget   leave   happen   not ask   be (x2)
> get back   see   have (x2)   stay   go

1 A: _____ anyone _____ my pen?
   B: What does it look like?
   A: It's silver. I'm sure I _____ it on the table before we _____ to lunch.

2 A: _____ you _____ to Kiera today?
   B: No, and I _____ her yet if she wants to come out with us tomorrow.

3 A: Hi, Suzie. When _____ you _____ from vacation?
   B: A few days ago, but I _____ already _____ it. There _____ over 300 emails in my inbox!
   A: I sympathize! The same thing _____ after my break.

4 A: Do you know anyone who _____ flu?
   B: No, thankfully. What about you?
   A: Frank _____ away from school last week because one of the other kids _____ a fever, but it was a false alarm.
   B: Yes, so far everyone in my family _____ OK.

VOCABULARY *PLUS*
WORD BUILDING: NOUNS

5 A Complete the quotes with the noun form of the words in capitals.

1 "_____ is never without a reason, but seldom with a good one."
Benjamin Franklin, US diplomat and inventor
ANGRY

2 "The chief enemy of _____ is 'good' sense."
Pablo Picasso, Artist
CREATIVE

3 "There is no such thing as pure pleasure; some _____ always goes with it."
Ovid, poet
ANXIOUS

4 "Most things in life are moments of pleasure and a lifetime of _____; photography is a moment of _____ and a lifetime of pleasure."
Tony Benn, politician
EMBARRASSED

5 "There can be no deep _____ where there is not deep love."
Martin Luther King Jr., civil rights activist
DISAPPOINTED

6 "If I ever completely lost my _____, I would be frightened half to death."
Paul Lynde, actor
NERVOUS

7 "Prayer is not an old woman's idle _____. Properly understood and applied, it is the most potent instrument of action."
Mahatma Gandhi, leader and activist
AMUSED

8 "Men lose more conquests by their own _____ than by any virtue in the woman."
Ninon de L'Enclos, writer
AWKWARD

9 "A life of _____ is inevitable for any coach whose main enjoyment is winning."
Chuck Noll, American football coach
FRUSTRATED

B Check (✓) the quotations you agree with and put an ✗ next to those you don't agree with.

parentheses / movie   brackets / film
vacation / sympathize   holiday / sympathise

VOCABULARY
ADS

1 Complete the ads with the words in the box.

| refundable | negotiable | for | in |
| sign | enrollment | trial | |

CIRCUIT TRAINING

LIMITED ¹_____
—ONLY TWO PLACES LEFT!

² _____ up now.
Fill ³ _____ your personal information on this form and pay the deposit today!

(Deposit is non-⁴_____)

TRY THIS AMAZING APP

New Life-organizer app is now available for Android users. There is a free ⁵_____ for the first month.

GUYS & GALS

Discount tickets available for matinée performance. Seating is limited, so buy now! Prices are non-⁶_____, and two-⁷_____-one deal does not apply to this show.

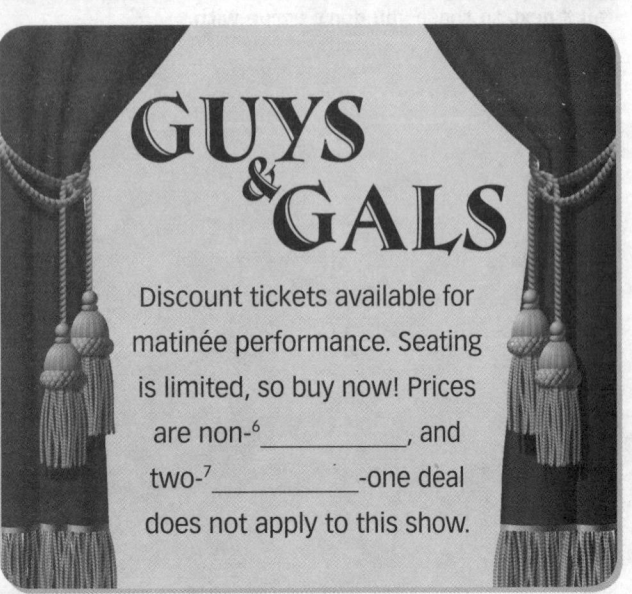

FUNCTION
POLITE INQUIRIES

2 Correct two mistakes in each sentence.

1 I'm like to inquire for a reservation I made.
2 I was wandering is that would be possible.
3 Would there be any chances of get the same price for the following weekend?
4 I am really grateful you could make an exception.
5 Would your mind saying me why it's so complicated to change?
6 Do you me mind asking what is your name?
7 Will you mind transfer me to your supervisor.

 3 Listen to the intonation of the inquiries. Write polite (P) or impolite (I).

1 a) _P_   b) _____
2 a) _____   b) _____
3 a) _____   b) _____
4 a) _____   b) _____
5 a) _____   b) _____
6 a) _____   b) _____
7 a) _____   b) _____

LEARN TO
MANAGE INQUIRIES

4 A Put the words in the correct order to make sentences.

a) transferring / you / mind / would / me / ?
_____

b) that / just / difficult, / it's / be / sorry / to / …
_____

c) a / me / with / minute / bear / .
_____

d) question, / keeping / have / you / I / one / if / I'm / more / not / .
_____

e) you / keep / to / sorry / .
_____

f) hold / minute? / just / you / a / I'll / can / on / see / .
_____

B Listen to the conversation and read the audio script on page 74. Check (✓) the sentences above which are used. Which sentence is not used?

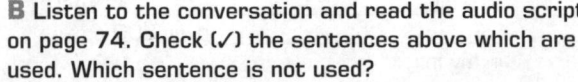

enrollment / personal information
Life-organizer

enrolment / personal details
Life-organiser

VOCABULARY
ISSUES

1 A Write the problem for each headline. The first letters are given.

LOCAL PEOPLE REJECT PLANNED POWER STATION

1 do _____

Electricity and Gas Prices Rise by 23%

2 ec _____

NUMBER OF PEOPLE SLEEPING ON CITY STREETS RISING

3 ur _____

PRESIDENT ASKS FOR CHANGES IN GOVERNMENT

4 po _____

OCEAN TEMPERATURES RISE BY 0.5°C

5 gl _____

RAILWAY WORKERS GO ON STRIKE

6 in _____

PRIVACY AT RISK FROM INTERNET COMPANIES

7 et _____

NO RAIN FOR FOURTH MONTHS – FARMERS WORRIED

8 ru _____

B Listen and check.

C Listen again and write the words next to the correct stress pattern.

Oo _____ _____ _____
Ooo _____
oOo _____
oOoo _____ _____
ooOo _____

GRAMMAR
PRESENT PERFECT SIMPLE AND CONTINUOUS

2 A Match the beginnings a) and b) with the endings i) and ii).

1 a) She's done
   b) She's been doing
   i) her homework since she got home from school.
   ii) all her homework.

2 a) I've sent
   b) I've been sending
   i) twenty-five application letters this morning.
   ii) application letters all morning. I need a break!

3 a) Pete's called
   b) Pete's been calling
   i) you all evening. Is your cell on?
   ii) and left you a message.

4 a) I've read this magazine.
   b) I've been reading this magazine.
   i) Do you want to borrow it when I've finished?
   ii) Do you want to borrow it?

5 a) Julia's gone to the gym—
   b) Julia's been going to the gym
   i) and she's twenty pounds lighter now.
   ii) would you like me to ask her to call you back?

6 a) The temperature has dropped
   b) The temperature has been dropping
   i) all day.
   ii) to minus twenty-two.

B Listen to the sentences and repeat what you hear. Pay attention to the stress and rhythm.

3 Complete the blog post with the present perfect simple or continuous form of the verbs in parentheses. If both are possible, use the continuous form.

I ¹_____ (travel) all my life, and I ²_____ (visit) more than twenty-five countries, many of them less rich than my own. I ³_____ (often / want) to take something to repay people for their hospitality, but I ⁴_____ (never / know) what to choose. Anyway, recently I ⁵_____ (explore) a number of websites that give advice, and I ⁶_____ (find) a great one called stuffyourruck-sack.com. It was created by Kate Humble, who ⁷_____ (host) wildlife programs on television for many years. It's a beautifully simple idea: the website matches up charities that need stuff with people who are willing to provide and deliver it. Travelers ⁸_____ (tell) the website about 187 organizations in eighty-one countries, and these include schools needing books or soccer balls, orphanages needing clothes and toys and trade organizations needing cells. So far it looks as if the response ⁹_____ (be) good, and the website ¹⁰_____ (recently / appear) in a "Find of the Year" survey of new sites.

cell / twenty pounds / soccer balls   mobile / ten kilos / footballs

2.1

LISTENING

4 A Read the text and answer the questions.

1 What is the aim of the organization? How does it want to achieve it?
_____

2 Which of the ideas 1–8 are connected to the environment (E) and which are connected to personal and social development (PS)?

> In 2004, a small London-based community organization called *We Are What We Do* published a book, *Change the world for a fiver**. It contained fifty simple actions which ordinary people could do to make the world a better place. Now it is a global movement with a lively website, millions of active participants and more than 130 ideas for actions.
>
> Its motto is:
>
> **SMALL ACTIONS × LOTS OF PEOPLE = BIG CHANGE.**

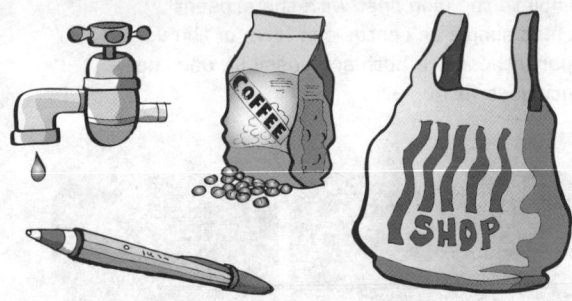

1 Use a **pen** from start to finish ___E___
2 Smile and smile back _____
3 Do something you think you are unable to do _____
4 Buy fairly traded products _____
5 Remember people's names _____
6 Turn off the **faucet** when you brush your teeth _____
7 Say "no" to plastic bags whenever possible _____
8 Learn one good joke _____

*$5

B Listen to four people speaking about their experiences. Which ideas 1–8 in the text in Exercise 4A did each one try?

1 ____ 2 ____ 3 ____ 4 ____ ____

C Listen again and make notes about:

a) why the speaker chose that particular action.
b) what problems each speaker experienced.

Speaker 1 a) _____
          b) _____
Speaker 2 a) _____
          b) _____
Speaker 3 a) _____
          b) _____
Speaker 4 a) _____
          b) _____

VOCABULARY *PLUS*
VERBS/NOUNS WITH THE SAME FORM

5 A Complete the sentences with the correct form of the words in the box.

> decrease   project   record   permit   appeal

1 In the 2008 Olympics, Usain Bolt set three world _____ including the 100 meters.
2 If you stay in Spain for more than ninety days, you need to apply for a resident's _____.
3 CCTV cameras have been successful, with a huge _____ in incidents of violence.
4 Police have made a nationwide _____ for help to find a missing sixteen-year-old.
5 The National Gallery is planning to _____ gigantic images of Picasso paintings onto the outside of the building.
6 The Water for You scheme is a _____ to give hundreds of people access to clean water.
7 Researchers _____ South American river turtles talking to each other underwater.
8 The amount of ice at the South Pole _____ significantly over the last ten years.
9 Students _____ to work and study in this country.
10 Environmentalists _____ to supermarkets to reduce the amount of food waste.

B Listen and check your answers.

C Listen again and underline the stress in the words you wrote in Exercise 5A.

records

pen / faucet   biro / tap

READING

1 A You are going to read about a course that trains people to be spies. Read the list and check (✓) the three things that you think are most important for a spy to be able to do.

a) break into a property
b) drive fast without getting into an accident
c) follow someone without getting caught
d) pretend they are someone else
e) use karate or other martial arts
f) win the trust of a stranger

B Read the article. Which three things from the list above are mentioned?

1 _____ 2 _____ 3 _____

C Match the quotes a)–e) with one of the paragraphs in the article.

a) I had to get right underneath, and it was difficult to attach it securely.
b) I'm a location manager for a TV company, and we need a place to film.
c) I'm going on safari, and I'll be back in two months.
d) It's just another thing that girls do better than boys!
e) I used to work at a men's clothing store on Madison Avenue—that's how I got this job.

D Find words and phrases in the article that match definitions 1–8.

1 can't replace (paragraph 1) _is no substitute for_
2 fast and intensive period of training (paragraph 1) _____
3 someone who wants to be something; potential (paragraph 2) _____
4 believable (paragraph 3) _____
5 become unnoticeable (paragraph 4) _____
6 work secretly with a different identity (paragraph 5) _____
7 look similar to everything around you (paragraph 6) _____
8 tell secrets to (paragraph 6) _____

SO YOU WANT TO BE A SPY?

Despite recent developments in surveillance technology, a camera is no substitute for the human eye, and there will always be a need for that most secretive of professions, the spy. In the BBC3 series, *Spy*, a group of eight volunteers took a two-month crash course in spying. Their trainers were former spies and experts in fields such as psychology and body language.

Before they joined the course, the would-be spies were allowed to tell only one person what they were really doing; for everyone else, they had to invent a believable cover story to explain their two-month absence. A couple of them immediately got into trouble when their story of a two-month job in New York resulted in friends promising to visit them.

As soon as they arrived at headquarters and before they had time to unpack, the eight "spies" faced their first challenge: they had just ten minutes to talk their way into the apartment of a complete stranger and be seen by their trainers drinking a glass of water on the balcony. It's a great task and one often used by real spy agencies to test their spies' abilities to act under pressure and think up plausible reasons to gain access to places.

The recruits learned about surveillance techniques including how to "go gray" and disappear into a crowd and also how to organize a surveillance operation on a house. This meant breaking into the property, planting secret cameras and bugs and attaching tracking devices to cars.

Another week, the recruits had to go undercover, adopt new identities and take temporary jobs in a gym, a clothing store and a barber's. They had to convince their co-workers that they were genuine, gain their trust and finally persuade one of them to do something wrong, for example, to lie or to sign a false document.

At the end of the experience, what qualities did they think were important for being a spy? "A spy needs to be a quick thinker, work well under pressure and be able to blend in." It helps to be a woman: "Sandy, our female trainer, loved to remind us how women made better spies." So if you are a tall male, it's probably not worth applying. And were any of the participants eager to become a spy? Certainly not one married candidate: "A Service insider told me that there is an exceptionally high divorce rate in the spy business with a lot of agents marrying their secretaries—the only person they can confide in and trust."

VOCABULARY

SURVEILLANCE

2 Complete the sentences. The first letters are given.

1 When you *id*_____ someone or something, you recognize and correctly name someone or something.
2 People or organizations that are in charge of a particular country or area are called the *au*_____.
3 If something is a *de*_____ to crime, it acts to reduce the chance of it happening.
4 To *st*_____ information is to keep facts in a computer or in a file.
5 To find information on a computer is to *ac*_____ data.
6 Carefully watch something over a period of time, for example a nurse *mo*_____ a patient's condition.
7 Crime *pr*_____ is all about stopping something bad from happening before it occurs.
8 If you *ke*_____ *tr*_____ of someone who is moving, you always know their position.

clothing store / eager clothes shop / keen

GRAMMAR
THE PASSIVE

3 A Complete the sentences with the passive form of the verbs in parentheses.

STRANGE BUT TRUE!

1 All gondolas in Venice, Italy must _____ (paint) black unless they belong to a high official.

2 The modern Frisbee _____ (invent) by the Frisbie Pie Company in 1946 when their pie tins _____ (throw) around by employees during breaks.

3 Over the centuries, Korea _____ (invade) more times than any other country in the world.

4 The white surface of the Taj Mahal _____ (gradually / damage) by pollution and is turning yellow.

5 British guidebooks in the nineteenth century advised women to put pins in their mouths to avoid _____ (kiss) in the dark when trains went through tunnels.

6 You are more likely _____ (kill) by a champagne cork than a poisonous spider, but most people are more afraid of spiders.

7 Kangaroos can _____ (find) in the wild in only two countries: Australia and New Zealand.

8 When Christopher Columbus "discovered" America in 1492, the continent _____ (already / explore) by the Vikings from Norway over three centuries earlier.

B Two of the facts above are false. Which are they?

4 Complete the sentences with the correct active or passive form of the verbs in parentheses.

TECHNOLOGY UPDATE

Currently hundreds of trainee medical students ¹_____ (teach) through the online virtual world *Second Life*. Once a day, students ²_____ (send) to locations in the online world to treat computer-generated patients. When they are there, virtual equipment can ³_____ (use) to check the patients at the scene, and then the trainees can ⁴_____ (decide) on the best course of action. The training tool has been a great success so far, and starting next year it ⁵_____ (use) at a number of medical schools around the world.

Pollution is an ever-growing problem in our cities, but in the near future a new system ⁶_____ (allow) traffic managers to identify pollution hotspots. It ⁷_____ (be) possible to alter the movement of cars through the city by changing the traffic light sequencing to direct cars away from problem areas. A computer ⁸_____ (also / send) commuters warning text alerts on their cell phones so they can decide how to avoid the hotspot. The new pollution monitoring system ⁹_____ (test) successfully for the first time in a trial last month and could ¹⁰_____ (introduce) as soon as next year.

WRITING
A LETTER OF COMPLAINT; LEARN TO USE FORMAL WRITTEN LANGUAGE

5 A Correct the mistakes in the underlined phrases.

Dear Sir or Madam,

¹I am writing with regard for my stay in one of your hotels.

I stayed at the Riley Hotel in Belfast from June 14 to 16 and experienced a number of problems. First, the room had not been properly cleaned. Second, there were no tea- or coffee-making facilities in the room. Finally, there was a party in the room under mine, and it kept me awake until early morning.

I have already spoken to the hotel manager about this, but she was very rude and suggested that I write to you.

In order ²to dissolve this matter, I am requesting that you refund the money for my stay at the hotel. ³Please contract me within ten days of the date of this letter ⁴to convince that this step has been taken.

⁵Thank you for your promptly attention to this matter.

⁶Yours faithlessly,

Viola Gresham

B Write a letter of complaint (120–150 words) to a restaurant where you recently had an important lunch, e.g., a meeting or a first date. Include three things that went wrong.

FUNCTION
OPINIONS

1 A Cross out the unnecessary words in the underlined phrases.

A: Do you think students should be allowed to use their phones in class?

B: Yeah, ¹I'm not in favor of that. The way I see it is that students would be more motivated if they could use phones, maybe to make short movies or things like that.

A: Mm, ²I'm not being so sure, you know how kids are. ³It seems that to me that they'd just start texting each other whenever they were bored.

B: Mm, well, ⁴I'm agree to a certain extent. They would certainly need very strict rules, you know, about turning them on and off. But phones could be useful for things like practicing languages or setting homework reminders.

A: Yes, ⁵I can suppose so, but what about bullying, you know, kids sending each other nasty messages? Or phones could be a target for thieves.

B: ⁶Is fair enough, but either of those things could happen after school.

A: Hmm. ⁷I see your point is, but ⁸I'm still not so convinced. I think on balance, it's better to keep them out of classes.

B: ⁹I don't disagree. I think we should encourage them.

B Listen or read the audio script on page 75 to check.

C Listen to the opinion phrases and repeat what you hear.

But you said no cell phones in class.

LEARN TO
SUPPORT YOUR VIEWPOINT

2 Complete the second sentence so that it has a similar meaning to the first. Start with the words given.

1 The latest research has found that profiles on social networking sites are accurate descriptions of people's personalities.

According _____.

2 Kids still enjoy dolls, electric train sets and Lego.

Toys like _____.

3 Japan is one of many countries where fish is an important part of the diet.

In many countries, for instance _____.

4 People are said to be attracted to partners who look like them.

Apparently, people _____.

5 There is no evidence that coffee increases long-term memory.

As far as I know, _____.

6 Media studies, sports studies and dance are examples of "soft" subjects and are no longer being offered in some colleges.

"Soft" subjects such _____.

VOCABULARY
OPINION ADJECTIVES

3 A Put the letters in bold in the correct order to make adjectives. The first letter is underlined.

A: What are the drunk driving laws in your country?

B: Zero tolerance. It's ¹g**lelial** _____ to drive if you've drunk any alcohol at all.

A: That seems like a ²**r**asnoaeble _____ law to me.

A: Models shouldn't wear fur. It's ³**c**hutainel _____ to kill animals just for fashion.

B: I'd go along with you there, but what about in really cold places?

A: I think it's possible that one day everyone will have a microchip under their skin from birth.

B: Really? I find the whole idea deeply ⁴**b**irdugsint _____.

A: Jan's gone too far this time! His idea at the meeting was ⁵**u**regasout**o** _____!

B: I agree. I thought it was silly and ⁶**i**repsrsbenilo _____.

A: I entirely agree.

B Listen and write the adjectives next to the correct stress patterns.

Ooo _____

oOo _____ _____ _____

oOoo _____

ooOoo _____

C Listen again and repeat what you hear.

drunk driving  drink drive

R1 REVIEW 1: UNITS 1–2

GRAMMAR VERB TENSE REVIEW

1 Complete the article with the past simple, present perfect simple or present perfect continuous forms of the verbs in parentheses.

Grandmother Passes Driving Test on 950th Attempt

Cha Sa-soon ¹_____ (want) to drive for years, and last week she ²_____ (move) a step closer to that dream: she ³_____ (pass) the written exam for a driver's license on her 950th attempt.
"I ⁴_____ (try) to pass this test for over four years," said the sixty-eight-year-old grandmother. "And now I ⁵_____ (finally do) it. Over the past two years, a lot of people ⁶_____ (tell) me I'm crazy, but I don't mind. If you have a dream, you can't give up."
She ⁷_____ (become) a bit of a legend at the testing center. "It ⁸_____ (be) difficult to see her fail so many times," said the center director. "And we ⁹_____ (hope) that sooner or later she would get through. She'll be missed, that's for sure," he ¹⁰_____ (add). "A day without Cha is like a day without our favorite granny."
Mrs. Sa-soon ¹¹_____ (spend) over five million Korean won on fees so far; now she just needs to pass the practical test, and, after she ¹²_____ (pass) that, she'll be given a license.

2 Match the sentence halves.

1 I've never seen snow
2 I'd never seen snow
   a) until I went to Austria.
   b) in my life.
3 I couldn't find a job
4 I haven't been able to find a job
   a) after college.
   b) since college.
5 No one has seen her
6 She was last seen
   a) a week ago.
   b) in the past week.
7 I've been seeing a therapist
8 I've seen a therapist
   a) three times now.
   b) regularly.
9 Many students have been arriving late
10 Many students arrived late
   a) recently.
   b) the other day.
11 I thought I understood this
12 I've understood everything
   a) so far.
   b) before now.

driver's license  driving licence

VOCABULARY REVIEW

3 Complete the sentences with the correct words or phrases.

1 a people person/down-to-earth
   a) Lena's a _____: she loves talking to everyone she meets.
   b) Tessa will always tell you what she thinks, she's very _____.

2 awkward/embarrassed
   a) The article is called "Top health questions you are too _____ to ask."
   b) I was with my husband when we ran into his ex-wife. It was very _____.

3 relieved/impressed
   a) Beth thought she'd lost her passport, so she was incredibly _____ to find it.
   b) The boss seemed _____ with my work on the report, and he's giving me tomorrow off.

4 non-refundable/two-for-one
   a) The _____ deal is only available on Monday evenings.
   b) A _____ deposit is required when reserving the vacation.

5 monitor/keep track of
   a) When I'm working on a painting, I never _____ the time. It drives my wife crazy.
   b) We're going to try you on this new treatment, and we'll _____ your progress carefully.

6 identify/deterrent
   a) Are the fines working as a/an _____ to pollution?
   b) Can full body scanners at airports _____ illegal products coming into the country?

7 illegal/unethical
   a) Hunting elephants is _____, but hunting deer is allowed with a permit.
   b) Buying an essay from the Internet and saying you wrote it is totally _____.

8 disturbing/outrageous
   a) It was absolutely _____ that the workers were told of their layoffs by text message.
   b) I found the program about child beauty competitions slightly _____.

9 irresponsible/reasonable
   a) I think it's _____ to refuse to pay for the food—no one could eat it.
   b) Lending money to people who can't afford to pay it back is just _____.

4 A Look at the underlined sounds in each group. Circle the word with the different sound.

1 auth<u>o</u>rity, nerv<u>ou</u>s, <u>a</u>wkward
2 ident<u>i</u>fy, cr<u>i</u>me, rel<u>ie</u>ved
3 outr<u>a</u>geous, inform<u>a</u>tion, decre<u>a</u>se
4 w<u>i</u>tty, perm<u>i</u>t, disappo<u>i</u>nting
5 non-ref<u>u</u>ndable, <u>u</u>rban, fr<u>u</u>strated

B Listen and check. Then listen and repeat.

14

REVIEW 1: UNITS 1–2   R1

GRAMMAR DIRECT AND INDIRECT QUESTIONS

5 Change the direct questions into indirect questions.

1. What were you like ten years ago?
   Can you tell _____?
2. How do you think you've changed?
   I'd be interested _____.
3. What have you done that you are most proud of?
   Would you mind telling _____?
4. Is it possible for a person to stay the same all his life?
   I wonder _____.
5. Who has influenced you the most?
   Could you tell _____?
6. Would you like to direct a movie yourself?
   I was wondering _____.

VOCABULARY PLUS WORD BUILDING: NOUNS

6 Find and correct the mistakes in the formation of the words in bold.

The Worst Day of My Life

My first solo piano concert in the music academy—it should have been the best day of my life. Of course, I felt a touch of ¹**anxious** before the performance, and I arrived early only to find that they had replaced the piano that I had practiced on with a different one. The new piano wasn't bad, but because of my ²**nervous** and ³**frustrated** I made a lot of mistakes. I was very ⁴**disappointment** in myself, and it was all very ⁵**embarrassment**. Afterward, there was a lot of ⁶**awkward** at the reception, since people didn't know what to say. I wished the ground would swallow me up.

1 _____   4 _____
2 _____   5 _____
3 _____   6 _____

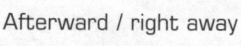
Afterward / right away

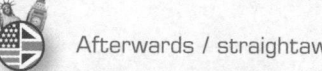
Afterwards / straightaway

FUNCTION POLITE INQUIRIES

7 A Underline the correct alternative(s).

1. Yes, Mr. Lawson. How can I *help/refund/answer* you?
2. I *was wondering/would wonder/wonder* whether I could move it to the week after.
3. And would there be any chance of *reserve/reserving/to reserve* for a friend?
4. *Could you/Would you mind/I'd appreciate* telling me if that's going to cost more?
5. *Can you/Could you/Do you* tell me why I've been kept on hold for so long? It's really annoying.
6. I'd *appreciate it/thank you/be grateful* if you could put it in an email.

B Match replies a)–f) to inquiries 1–6 above.

a) The computers are extremely slow today. I'm very sorry.
b) Just a moment. Sorry, you've just taken the last place.
c) Of course. I'll confirm all the details right away.
d) Sorry to keep you. That will be 250 dollars extra.
e) I'm calling to inquire about a reservation I made last week.
f) Bear with me a minute. Yes, that reservation is transferable.

VOCABULARY ISSUES

8 Read the clues and complete the crossword.

Across

1. An issue about principles of what is right and wrong.
5. A problem relating to trade, industry and the management of money.
7. This problem happens in or is related to the countryside.
8. This social issue relates to the government, politics and public affairs of a country.

Down

2. A problem that relates to industry or the people working in it.
3. This issue affects or includes the whole world.
4. These issues happen in one particular country and do not involve any other countries.
6. A problem relating to towns and cities.

15

R1 REVIEW 1: UNITS 1–2

VOCABULARY PLUS VERBS/NOUNS WITH THE SAME FORM

9 A Complete the news reports with the correct form of the words in the box.

> decrease research import desert produce
> fine record project appeal permit

A group of rock stars are ¹_____ for people to fund a new ²_____ aimed at preventing malaria. Recent medical ³_____ shows there is a dramatic ⁴_____ in the disease when malaria nets are provided for families.

Fifty-two tourists have been rescued from the ⁵_____ near the Step Pyramid in Egypt after temperatures reached 49 degrees Celsius —the highest level ever ⁶_____ in the area. The tourists were stranded when their bus broke down. The group's tour operator has been arrested for failing to obtain a ⁷_____ to conduct business in the area and has been ordered to pay a ⁸_____.

And in business, a number of European countries are planning to cut ⁹_____ from the United States as trade tensions continue. The USA has recently increased taxes on ¹⁰_____ coming from abroad to an all-time high.

B Listen or read the audio script on pages 75–76 to check.

C Underline the stress in words 1–10. Then listen and check.

GRAMMAR THE PASSIVE

10 Complete the articles with the active or passive form of the verbs in the boxes.

> think score complete ask

Improve Your IQ

In a recent experiment, two groups of people ¹_____ to spend time writing down some sentences, one group about a typical college professor and the other about a soccer hooligan. They then ²_____ a trivia test. The result: the "professor" group ³_____ much higher than the other group. It ⁴_____ that this is due to "priming" the brain in a positive way to get it to think more intelligently.

> cause film predict ask

Together forever?

In an experiment that is being carried out in the USA, married couples ⁵_____ having a conversation. They ⁶_____ to discuss topics that ⁷_____ some friction in their relationship in the past. Based on just several minutes of the material, it can ⁸_____ with high accuracy who will still be together in fifteen years and who will divorce.

> find give face design

CARE BEARS FOR THE ELDERLY?

In the coming years, many countries ⁹_____ the challenge of an aging population and a shortage of nurses. The Japanese-produced Robo-bear ¹⁰_____ to help with tasks such as lifting and moving patients. The first human-shaped robots ¹¹_____ to be too frightening for patients, and so now the Robo-bear ¹²_____ the head of a friendly cartoon bear.

FUNCTION OPINIONS

11 Put the words in the correct order.

1 your / I / but / point, / see
_____

2 of / in / that / favor / I'm
_____

3 with / don't / you / agree / I
_____

4 extent, / certain / a / to / but / agree / I
_____

5 not / still / I'm / convinced
_____

6 what / mean / I / see / you
_____

7 not / sure / so / I'm
_____

16

REVIEW 1: UNITS 1–2 R1

CHECK

Circle the correct option to complete the sentences.

1. Do you know _____?
   a) she's going   b) whether she's going
   c) where is she going

2. Sign up for the classes as soon as you can—there is _____, so do it as soon as possible.
   a) limited enrollment   b) fill out your information
   c) free trial

3. A: Your clothes are soaking wet!
   B: Yes, I _____ in the rain.
   a) walked   b) 've walked   c) 've been walking

4. _____ violence is a growing problem in times of unemployment.
   a) Domestic   b) Economic   c) Global

5. They _____ the report for days, and it's still not finished.
   a) 've been writing   b) 've written
   c) 've been written

6. Could you tell me _____?
   a) what means that   b) what that means
   c) what does that mean

7. I'm calling _____ a course.
   a) to inquire about   b) about inquiring
   c) inquire about

8. Corruption isn't only deeply _____, it's also _____.
   a) disturbing/irresponsible   b) reasonable/unethical
   c) disturbing/unethical

9. We need to _____ all their comings and goings over the next twenty-four hours.
   a) keep track of   b) surveillance   c) permit

10. I felt some _____ when I couldn't make myself understood in Spanish.
    a) frustrating   b) frustration   c) frustrated

11. Teachers want _____ what students don't like.
    a) to tell   b) to be told   c) being told

12. I hate speaking in public—I always get very _____.
    a) nerves   b) nervousness   c) nervous

13. I _____ Rita recently. Is she OK?
    a) didn't see   b) haven't yet seen   c) haven't seen

14. A: What _____?
    B: She's great! I really like her.
    a) 's your new boss like   b) does your new boss like
    c) 's like your new boss

15. My mom was _____ thrilled to hear the news.
    a) very   b) fairly   c) absolutely

16. I _____ ten cups of coffee, and it's only noon.
    a) had   b) 've had   c) 've been having

17. A: They really shouldn't have closed the school.
    B: I agree _____, but there were good reasons for it.
    a) for a certain extent   b) to a certain extent
    c) to a certain point

18. The president's _____ for the early release of the hostages has not been successful.
    a) project   b) appeal   c) record

19. Some say that a guard dog is the best _____ to crime.
    a) deterrent   b) monitor   c) access

20. We've been very lucky _____.
    a) yet   b) already   c) so far

21. They found out that all their movements _____ by CCTV cameras.
    a) were being monitored   b) were monitoring
    c) have monitored

22. Would there be _____ holding my place?
    a) any chance for   b) any chance of
    c) any chance

23. She's been feeling a lot of _____ about the new job—that's why she can't sleep.
    a) amusement   b) anxiety   c) creativity

24. _____ the minimum voting age being decreased to sixteen.
    a) I totally disagree   b) I'm against
    c) I see your point

25. The most _____ way forward seems to be to organize a meeting to discuss the issue calmly.
    a) reasonable   b) irresponsible   c) outrageous

26. The murderer _____ yet.
    a) hasn't caught   b) wasn't caught
    c) hasn't been caught

27. There are lots of homeless people sleeping in the streets. It's the capital city's greatest _____ problem.
    a) industrial   b) rural   c) urban

28. He always knows a good joke; he's _____.
    a) a good laugh   b) a computer geek
    c) down-to-earth

29. You got the highest grade on the exam? I'm really _____.
    a) relieved   b) anxious   c) impressed

30. He _____ once last week.
    a) hasn't visited   b) didn't visit   c) has visited

RESULTS /30

calling / mom / grade on the exam   phoning / mum / mark in the exam

3 stories

3.1

GRAMMAR
NARRATIVE TENSES

1 A Underline the correct alternative.

1 One day the old man *fished/was fishing* as usual when he *saw/was seeing* something shiny in the water.

2 In 1995 Ella *was teaching/taught* in the Sudan and *became/had become* well known locally as the "Canadian lady".

3 I *'d known/'d been knowing* Javier for many years, and, when I *read/was reading* he was in prison, I knew there must be a mistake.

4 He *noticed/was noticing* that someone *had left/had been leaving* a briefcase on the park bench.

5 The prince *had been searching/was searching* in the forest for over ten hours and *began/was beginning* to lose hope.

6 Ella *had looked/had been looking* through old photo albums all morning when she *heard/was hearing* a knock on the door, and that moment inspired the lyrics to her greatest hit.

7 By that evening the children *were/had been* exhausted and hungry because they *'d walked/'d been walking* in the forest all day with nothing to eat.

8 We *'d driven/'d been driving* 18 miles when the engine suddenly stopped; someone *took/had taken* most of the gas out of the car, someone who wanted us dead.

B Which of the sentences above do you think come from: a detective story (D), a traditional folk tale (F) or a biography of someone's life (B)?

2 Complete the sentences with the past perfect simple or the past perfect continuous form of the verbs in parentheses. If both are possible, use the past perfect continuous.

1 In the morning everything was white because it _____ (snow) all night.

2 "How long _____ (the victim/come) to this club?" Logan asked.

3 My brother was furious because I _____ (break) his MP3 player.

4 How much money _____ (you/make) by the time you were twenty?

5 I had a sore throat because I _____ (sing) all evening.

6 _____ (she/ever/do) anything like that before?

7 They _____ (not plan) to move, but a apartment became available suddenly.

8 The computer _____ (make) strange noises since the installation of the new software.

3 A Complete the news story with the correct form of the verbs in the box. There may be more than one possibility.

> fail rush begin bring feel realize
> sit seem overhear explain climb
> use change tell

An eight-year-old boy has been rescued by an enterprising Bangkok firefighter.

The boy from Thailand is autistic* and
1_____ very nervous before his first day of school, but initially he
2_____ to be OK. However, during the first lesson, his teacher
3_____ something to the class when she 4_____ that the boy 5_____ out of the window. "He 6_____ just outside the window with his legs swinging over the edge."

The rescue services were called in when the boy's mother 7_____ (also) to get the boy down. Everyone
8_____ to run out of ideas when one of the firefighters, Somchai Yoosabai,
9_____ the boy's mother talking about her son's love of superheroes. The quick-thinking fireman
10_____ back to the fire station and 11_____ into his Spider-Man costume. (Until then, Mr. Somchai
12_____ the costume to make school fire drills more interesting.)
"I 13_____ him, 'Spider-Man is here to rescue you. No monsters are going to attack you.'" The sight 14_____ a smile to the youngster's face, and he immediately walked into his rescuer's arms.

*A person who is autistic has a learning disability; it's difficult for them to communicate and form relationships.

B Listen to the news story above. For each verb 1–14 underline the main stressed syllable and write any weak forms: /ə/ or /ɪ/.

C Listen again and read the news story at the same time as the speaker. Pay attention to the stress and weak forms in the verbs.

18 miles / gas   30 km / petrol

LISTENING

4 A According to research, there are only seven types of stories or "plots." Match plots 1–7 with descriptions a)–g). Then listen and check your ideas.

1 overcoming the monster
2 rags to riches
3 the quest
4 voyage and return
5 comedy
6 tragedy
7 rebirth

a) The hero/heroine goes on a long, dangerous journey to achieve a goal.
b) A hero/heroine defeats a terrifying beast and saves others or wins a reward.
c) After misunderstandings and confusion, everything ends happily. It doesn't have to be funny but it often is.
d) A person leaves home and goes to a strange place. After adventures, he/she comes back.
e) Someone is in a terrible situation and then returns to happiness or is freed, often by the power of love.
f) An ordinary person discovers special talents or beauty in himself/herself and often gains great wealth.
g) A character follows a course of action which destroys him/her. This story always has a bad ending.

B Listen again. Which plot are the following connected to?

1 computer games   _____
2 Superman   _____
3 *Romeo and Juliet* _____
4 detective stories   _____
5 humor   _____
6 *Lost*   _____
7 losing money   _____

VOCABULARY

SAYINGS

5 Complete the sayings. Use the prompts to help you.

1 We may fail, but we won't know unless we try. As they say, *"nothing / venture / gain"*.
_____

2 Sue lost her job recently, but *cloud / silver / lining*, and now she has a better one.
_____

3 Li always gave money to a beggar, and one day the beggar saved him from a mugger. It's certainly true that *go / around / come / around*.
_____

4 I'm learning to bargain in markets. I've decided, *Rome / do / Romans / do*.
_____

5 No more second-hand computers for me—this one keeps breaking down. *Once / bite / twice / shy*.
_____

WRITING

A STORY

6 A Read the story. Which saying 1–3 does the story illustrate?

1 Every cloud has a silver lining.
2 What goes around comes around.
3 Once bitten, twice shy.

Once, as a lion was sleeping, a mouse passed by and ¹_____ woke him up; ²_____ the lion was angry and wanted to eat the mouse. The mouse ³_____ said she was very sorry and promised to help the lion in the future. The lion laughed ⁴_____ at this, but let her go because she had made him laugh.

Months later, the mouse ⁵_____ got her chance to help the lion when he was tied to a tree by some hunters. When the lion roared, ⁶_____ the mouse was nearby and came running. She tried to eat through the rope; it was very thick, but ⁷_____ she ate through it ⁸_____ and freed the lion. And the moral of the story is …

B Complete the story in Exercise 6A with adverbs from the box or adverbs of your own.

> stupidly   fortunately   naturally   eventually
> immediately   finally   completely   loudly

C Use the notes below to write the story (80–100 words). Use at least three adverbs from Exercise 6B to make your story more interesting.

The crow and the water pot: thirsty crow—find—water pot—water at the bottom—can't reach; at first—stare at pot—try to think what to do; clever plan—drop—small stones—one by one—water rise—top—crow drink; moral: "Necessity is the mother of invention."

humor   humour

3.2

VOCABULARY
ADJECTIVES FOR STORIES

1 Put the letters in bold in the correct order to make adjectives. The first letter is underlined.

1 The movie ending was very **rdaicmta** _dramatic_ — I could hardly watch it.
2 That play was absolutely **hrailoisu** _____. I nearly cried with laughing.
3 The life of Gandhi is very **isnrinigp** _____.
4 I found that poem about war very **tpoiangn** _____.
5 Jane is very **tnnseei** _____—she's very focused when she speaks to you.
6 Brian finished his 3,000 word movie review last night—that's **kareblmear** _____!
7 I really liked the end of the movie, the special effects were **dibleeincr** _____.
8 The story of the children was very **gimonv** _____—it nearly made me cry.

GRAMMAR
I WISH, IF ONLY

2 A Complete the survey results with the correct form of the verbs in parentheses. In some sentences you need to make the verb negative.

---

no regrets   HOME   NEWS   **SURVEY**   SEARCH

Regrets, we've had a few …

A survey of over-30s suggests that many people share the same regrets about the past. Some of the results are unsurprising, but others are unexpected. The top regrets are:

- One in ten people wishes they ¹_____ (work) abroad at some stage in their life.
- Just under a quarter of people wish they ²_____ (save) more money in their twenties.
- A quarter of people wish they ³_____ (begin) smoking.
- Nearly a third of people wish they ⁴_____ (pay) more attention at school.
- One in three people wishes that they ⁵_____ (get married) so young.
- Many people wish they ⁶_____ (leave) full-time education so early and regret that they didn't go to college.
- Almost a half of people wish they ⁷_____ (learn) a musical instrument.
- The top regret of all? Nearly half of people wish they ⁸_____ (travel) more when they were younger.

B Check (✓) the items you also regret.

3 A Listen and underline the alternative you hear.

1 I wish *I had/I'd had* more money.
2 I wish *I'd/you'd* worked harder at school.
3 I wish *it would stop/it had stopped* raining.
4 If only we*'ve/'d* told her.
5 If only we *went/'d gone* to the party.
6 If only you*'d/hadn't* turned it off.

B Listen again and repeat. Pay attention to the stress and the contractions: *'d* /əd/ and *hadn't* /ˈhædənt/.

4 Complete the second sentence so that it has a similar meaning to the first. Use between two and five words including the word given.

1 She can't stand the way the press keeps asking her about her private life.
STOP
She wishes the press _____ about her private life.

2 I'd prefer to be at home right now; it's too cold here.
HOME
I wish _____ right now; it's too cold here.

3 It's terrible—we owe so much money!
ONLY
If _____ so much money.

4 They didn't tell him the cost before he started the treatment.
TOLD
If _____ him the cost of the treatment before he started it.

5 I hate it when you interrupt me.
ME
I wish _____.

6 That's a great idea! Why didn't I think of it?
WISH
I _____ of that idea.

7 Wayne wishes he'd kept his temper.
KEPT
If only Wayne _____ his temper.

8 I can't see anything from here.
SEE
If only _____ from here.

9 Unfortunately, we don't have enough time.
MORE
If _____ time.

10 You just didn't listen to me!
LISTENED
I wish _____ to me!

READING

5 A Read the article and answer the questions.

1 What is the challenge each person faces?
2 How do they manage in their professions?

Our Series on People Who Have Achieved Success in Their Field in the Face of Extraordinary Challenges

For more than thirty years, soprano **Janine Roebuck** has delighted audiences with her singing in opera and musical theater. For most of that time, she has kept a closely guarded secret: she is profoundly deaf.

Janine comes from a family with hereditary deafness. At first, she thought she had escaped the disability, but at college she was diagnosed with progressive loss of hearing and was advised to give up her dream of a singing career. However, Janine decided to hide the truth from fellow musicians. Janine believed that she would not be employed as a singer if people knew about her disability because they would see it as a major problem. So she developed coping strategies to enable her to perform. When she sang with another person, she watched their breathing so that she could come in at the right time. She felt vibrations from the music, and occasionally she asked her fellow performers to tap the beat on her back.

Now Janine has decided to reveal the truth. Instead of being terrified of being found out, the singer is proud of her achievements and is using her story as an example to encourage other people with disabilities. As the word about Janine's deafness spreads, responses include astonishment and admiration. One conductor turned to the orchestra after she sang and told them she was deaf. Their applause delighted her.

If you listen to **Dean Du Plessis** on the radio, you will hear an articulate sports commentator with a comprehensive knowledge of cricket. It's incredible then to realize that Zimbabwean Du Plessis has never actually seen a game because he has been blind from birth.

How does he do it? He says his heightened sense of hearing compensates for his lack of sight. He uses microphones placed around the ground to help. Dean listens to the sound of the players during the game. He can tell who is who by the sound they make when they hit a ball or run across the pitch. Each player runs differently, for example, some players run in a particular way or use more effort than others. He also listens to the sounds when the bat strikes the ball, as well as the crowd.

Born near Harare, Zimbabwe, Du Plessis was lucky enough to attend the famous Worcester School for the Blind in South Africa. At school, much to the annoyance of his schoolmates, he would stay up late in the evening and do commentaries alongside the radio. One evening, a teacher overheard him commentating and told him to take it up as a profession because he was exceptionally good at it.

In 2001 Dean tried out with the microphone at Harare Sports Club and since then has never looked back. His passion and knowledge make him enormously popular with listeners and leave visiting teams and his co-commentators awestruck.

B Who do you think said the following: Janine (J) or Dean (D)?

1 It was a terrible blow to me.
2 It can be a sharp crack or a quieter sound.
3 Until then, I thought I was one of the lucky ones.
4 Your other senses become more acute.
5 I refused to give up.
6 Why now? Well, with age you don't really care so much.

C Try to complete the collocations below. Then read the text again to check your ideas.

1 a _____ secret
 = a well-kept secret
2 _____ deaf
 = completely deaf
3 to _____ a strategy
 = to invent and improve on a technique
4 to _____ the truth
 = to tell the truth after hiding it
5 a _____ knowledge
 = a complete knowledge
6 a _____ sense of hearing
 = increased sense of hearing

VOCABULARY PLUS
MULTI-WORD VERBS

6 A Complete the questions in the interview by adding *for*, *out*, *on*, *away*, *by* or *up*.

A: So you were brought ¹_____ by the ocean?
B: Yes, when I was growing ²_____, I practically lived underwater.
A: And when you started taking pictures, you picked it ³_____ quickly?
B: Yeah, I loved it, and I was good at it. I dropped ⁴_____ of college and went ⁵_____ to look for a job that combined my two great loves.
A: But at first you were unsuccessful at getting a job with the local companies.
B: That's right, and, as time went ⁶_____, I began to think I'd never get a job. Then I remembered a photographer I'd always looked ⁷_____ to. He was working at Global at that time.
A: Why did you take ⁸_____ such a key position with Global then?
B: I didn't, not at first. I was only an assistant on a documentary.
A: So did your boss resign from his position?
B: No. He was badly injured by a shark, so badly that he passed ⁹_____. It was terrible.
A: Oh, I'm sorry.
B: That's OK. Because I really admired him, I tried to bring all the things he stood ¹⁰_____ into my work: honesty, truth and realism. Now I get all the big movies.

B What is person B's job?

theater theatre

3.3

VOCABULARY
READING GENRES

1 Complete the crossword.

Across

3 A best-selling movie.
6 A webpage where people take part in online discussions is a website _____.
7 This website has facts and information about many different subjects.
9 A written story about fictional characters.
13 A book that someone writes about their own life.
14 A book that tells you how to do something, especially how to use a machine.
15 A short message on a social media website.

Down

1 The story someone writes about someone else's life.
2 A piece of writing about a particular subject is an online _____.
4 A type of website containing information or opinions from a particular person or about a particular subject. New information or comments are added regularly.
5 A _____ magazine is about the behavior and private lives of famous people.
8 Poems in general.
10 Japanese comics, often action-adventure, which are read by all ages.
11 The latest online news on an event or person is a social media _____.
12 The words of a song.

FUNCTION
EXPRESSING LIKES AND DISLIKES

2 A Complete B's part in each conversation.

1 **A:** What did you think of the book?
  B: [1]Well, / not / big fan / travel books
  _____

  A: Oh, why's that?
  B: [2]just / not / get into / all the description
  _____

2 **A:** I hear Nick's enjoying his new school.
  B: [3]Yes, what / he / love / about it / be / that they do / lot of sports
  _____

  A: I didn't know he liked sports.
  B: [4]Oh, yeah. / He / be / really into football / moment
  _____

3 **A:** Why don't you like barbecues?
  B: [5]not / stand / when the meat / not / cooked properly
  _____

B Listen and check your answers.

C Listen and underline between two and five main stresses in B's part. Listen again and say B's part at the same time as the recording.

LEARN TO
SUMMARIZE A PLOT

3 Complete the plot summary with the correct form of the verbs in the box.

> wait   fall (x2)   deliver   die   have   work
> earn   meet (x2)   kick out (x2)

As is true of many of his stories, there is an autobiographical element, with the life of the main character, Irek, bearing many resemblances to that of the author, André Hartowicz. In real life, Hartowicz, a political activist, [1]_____ of college for organizing protests against the administration. In the novel, the main character [2]_____ of college for signing a letter criticising the examination system. Hartowicz, before he became famous, [3]_____ as a waiter to pay his rent; in the story, Irek [4]_____ money as a postman. Hartowicz [5]_____ his first wife at a restaurant; she [6]_____ dinner with her husband while Hartowicz [7]_____ on tables, and they [8]_____ in love at first sight. In the story, however, Irek [9]_____ his wife-to-be when he [10]_____ a letter to her informing her that her husband [11]_____ in battle. They, too, [12]_____ in love at first sight.

sports   sport

22

LISTENING

1 A Read about the signs of addiction to social networking. Which ones are physical symptoms?

ARE YOU ADDICTED TO SOCIAL NETWORKING? THE SIGNS:
- forgetting to eat
- ignoring friends and family
- anxiety
- lying to spend time doing it
- very bad headaches
- always thinking about doing it
- sleep problems
- problems with school or work
- dry or aching eyes
- not taking appropriate breaks

B Listen to five people talking about their addictions. Write the number of the speaker (1–5) next to the signs in Exercise 1A. There may be more than one possibility.

C Listen again. Make two changes to each of the sentences (1–5) so they match what you hear.

1 I actually found it really strange talking to their face because I'm much more used to interacting with people online.
2 It's the quizzes and other applications that interest me, like there's always a new quiz or test for something.
3 I would often miss lunch so I could continue chatting.
4 To be fair, she probably asked me directly first, but I suppose I'd gotten so involved in the site that I didn't hear her.
5 When a chat message arrived, I couldn't resist. I'd stop what I was doing and join the chat.

VOCABULARY
FREE TIME

2 A Put the letters in the correct order to make verbs. The first letter is underlined.

1 whtc<u>i</u>s ffo _____
2 <u>o</u>csuf no _____
3 ll<u>c</u>ih _____
4 <u>r</u>cerhgae _____
5 urn<u>b</u> pu _____

B Complete the text with the correct form of the words in Exercise 2A.

My childhood was fairly happy. Our family wasn't well off, and we lived in a small crowded house, but that was OK. We had lots of arguments and fights but a lot of fun, too. Everything changed at school though. I couldn't deal with the discipline. I was always getting into trouble. I wouldn't ¹_____ the activities the teacher gave us—it wasn't that the class was boring, but I just couldn't concentrate. I used to ²_____ just at the time that I needed to pay attention. Then of course, I couldn't keep up with the other students. Worse than that, because I was the only student who didn't know what was happening in class, the other students used to ³_____ me _____ so that I'd get angry. Of course the teachers punished me for shouting at the other students. They would send me out of the class to ⁴_____ and calm down. As an adult, I still have these problems, but I know how to deal with them now. When I find myself losing focus, I go somewhere quiet to ⁵_____ and get some mental energy back. Then I come back to the task again—in a way, it's a bit like what happened at school.

GRAMMAR
PRESENT AND PAST HABITS

3 Underline the correct alternative.

1 I *didn't use to/don't usually* spend time with lots of people—I prefer to be alone.
2 I *used to/would* think I was right about everything, but these days I'm *used to/'m usually* more prepared to admit I'm wrong.
3 I *used to/would* like my little sister, but now she's grown up it's so annoying—she's *always/used to* using my stuff.
4 I *often have/'m often having* trouble understanding the local accent, so I think my English is worse than it *used to/would* be.
5 My friends and I would *take/taking* long walks, and we used to *stay/staying* out late every night.
6 Before I moved to this country, I used to *eating/eat* early. Here everyone eats very late, so I'm always *starving/starved* by the time I eat in the evening.
7 You're *always/used to* leaving your boots at the bottom of the steps. You *used to be/are always being* really neat.
8 I *used to/'m used to* write letters by hand, but now I'm *usually doing/usually do* everything on the computer.
9 A: Where's Dad?
   B: He*'ll be/is always being* in the garden. He's *always gardening/used to garden* nowadays.
10 Before my divorce, my wife *would/was used to* cook all my meals, but I generally *trying/try* to cook for myself now, and I'm getting better!
11 A: I hate always *having/have* to wear a uniform!
    B: What did you *use/used* to wear in your last school?
12 Mark and Amy were really competitive, they *would/'ll often* fight over little things. They*'ll still argue/are arguing* about small things even today.

appropiate / neat   proper / tidy

4.1

4 Listen to the phrases and underline the main stress in each sentence. Then listen and repeat.

1 I used to love it.
2 I didn't use to discuss it.
3 We'd always eat together.
4 We'd always argue.
5 He's not used to it yet.
6 They'll be in the park.
7 I was always getting into trouble.
8 He'll be at the office.

5 Complete the forum answers with the correct forms of *used to* or *would* and the verbs in parentheses. Use *would* where possible.

DO YOU FIND IT EASY TO CHANGE?

JonB We moved to Canada earlier this year, and we've found it difficult to cope with the cold winters. Before then, we ¹_____ (live) in New Mexico where the winters ²_____ (not be) so cold. The best piece of advice I was given was to invest in a very warm coat and hat!

Alex Two months ago, my doctor told me needed to eat less salt. Up to then, I ³_____ (put) about a spoonful of salt on a lot of things I ate. I ⁴_____ (think) food was tasteless without it, and I ⁵_____ (enjoy) meals without salt. At first it was difficult, but now whenever we eat out the food tastes too salty.

Vicki 2015 We have a new baby. Just two weeks old. We love him to bits, but he doesn't sleep at night. We ⁶_____ (have) at least eight hours' sleep. Now we're lucky if we get two hours before he wakes us up. We ⁷_____ (stay) in bed until mid-morning on the weekend—not now. In fact, we don't have a weekend any more!

Chloe OK I've just started my first job after college, and it's been a shock to the system! In college, I ⁸_____ (get up) at about nine o'clock, and now I have to be at work at nine. I also ⁹_____ (work) when I felt like working. Not now—my boss says when I work and when I have a break.

New Hubby I got married last month, and we've moved into our first apartment. I ¹⁰_____ (live) alone, so it's strange for me to share everything with someone, even my wife. Before, I ¹¹_____ (wash) the dishes whenever I wanted to, but my wife hates the mess, so I have to do it right away. Sometimes I wonder if I ¹²_____ (clean) my place regularly enough or if my wife is too neat.

WRITING

AN OPINION ESSAY; LEARN TO USE LINKERS

6 A Read the opinion essay. Which two paragraphs develop the positive side (P) of the argument and which paragraph develops the negative (N)?

A LIFELONG PARTNER SHOULD BE SOMEONE WHO HAS SIMILAR VALUES, PERSONALITY AND INTERESTS.
DO YOU AGREE?

1 Can you imagine being married to someone who is very different from you, in terms of their personality, beliefs or interests? In my view, it would be a recipe for disaster!

2 a) I believe it is vital that two people in a long-term relationship share the same basic values. b) If one of you believes that it is acceptable to read the other person's diary or emails and the other one doesn't, this could cause real problems.

3 c) I feel it is important that people have similar personalities and interests. d) Imagine you are an extroverted person who loves going out but you are married to someone who prefers to spend their evenings at home. Or e) consider a situation where one of you spends hours on their hobby but neglects their partner. The resulting tensions could put a serious strain on the relationship.

4 f) It is true that people can learn a lot from their differences. g) An outgoing person might help their shyer partner become more comfortable in social situations and therefore have more varied experiences than they might otherwise. This can lead to both people developing much more than they might if both of them were similar.

5 h) Although it is said that "opposites attract," it seems to me that the basis of a long-lasting relationship is having similar ideas, personalities and interests.

B Complete the essay with the linkers in the box. Write a)–h) next to the appropriate linker. Some can go in more than one position.

> to sum up,   for example,   as another example,
> at the same time,   in addition to this,   furthermore,
> to start with,   for instance,

C Write an opinion essay (200–250 words) on the following topic.

A true friendship is hard work. Do you agree?

wash the dishes / extroverted   do the washing-up / extrovert

READING

1 A Read the article quickly and write the paragraph number next to topics a)–e).

a) more recent developments
b) history and background
c) why you should read the article
d) space tourism for people who aren't rich
e) space hotels

B Read the article again and write true (T), false (F) or not given (NG) next to sentences 1–8. Underline the part of the article that helped you.

1 The writer thinks that business entrepreneurs are crazy.
2 Dennis Tito spent a week in space.
3 The Virgin Galactic flights stop at a space station but don't stay overnight.
4 The writer thinks that Tito should have bargained better.
5 The International Space Station doesn't have very luxurious facilities.
6 The Galactic Suite space hotel rotates to create gravity.
7 Some people think commercial space travel will be more and more competitive.
8 The writer recommends getting a job as a flight attendant.

C Find words and phrases in the article that match definitions 1–8.

1 the kind of thing that something is made of (paragraph 2)

2 people who doubt whether something is true or right (paragraph 2)

3 started thinking about how to solve a problem (paragraph 3)

4 following a path which does not go fully around the earth (paragraph 3)

5 thought of (paragraph 4)

6 aiming at (paragraph 4)

7 the normal cost (paragraph 5)

8 aggressive (paragraph 5)

SPACE TOURISM IS HERE!

 Fed up with the usual week-long vacation on the beach or walking through museums and old buildings that you only pretend to be interested in? Well, consider the ultimate in niche tourism: a new frontier, "the final frontier" in fact: space tourism.

 It wasn't long ago that space hotels were the stuff of science-fiction, and space tourism was a concept that only the craziest of business entrepreneurs talked about seriously. But since the 2001 flight of Dennis Tito, an American businessman, aboard a Russian Soyuz rocket, even skeptics have had to regard space tourism as an area with real commercial potential. In the first few years, a space tourist like Tito paid $20 million for a trip which included a week-long stay on the International Space Station.

 It was only a matter of time before the entrepreneurs got on the case, and UK entrepreneur Sir Richard Branson and his Virgin Galactic company have begun offering online reservations for sub-orbital flights aboard their SpaceShipTwo. Tickets start at $200,000, but are expected to come down in price to somewhere around $20,000s—almost a bargain compared to what Tito paid. But the Virgin flights are only two-and-a-half hours, taking passengers just beyond the 62-mile altitude that is the internationally defined boundary between Earth and space. Space tourists experience a few minutes of weightlessness and a view of the stars before heading back to Earth and gliding in for a landing. A German company has been working on providing a similar service called Project Enterprise.

 What about accommodations? A number of companies have come up with plans to develop space hotels that can offer more luxurious surroundings than the International Space Station, which was designed for research purposes, not for tourists. The Space Island Group planned a ring-shaped spacecraft, much like the one in the movie *2001: A Space Odyssey*, situated about 398 miles from Earth. The ring would rotate in order to create a gravitational pull so that tourists don't spend their space vacation floating in the air. Galactic Suite Ltd. was at one point targeting 2012 as the opening date for its luxury space hotel, with three-night stays going for $4.4 million—but that includes six weeks of training! And at least one international hotel chain has also expressed the intention of getting into the space hotel business.

 So is there a hope for ordinary folk who have run out of earthly destinations for their vacations but can't afford the going price for a seat on SpaceShipTwo or a few nights at the Galactic Suite space resort? Space enthusiasts are optimistic and encourage any would-be space tourist to keep saving up and expect prices to keep coming down as competition gets more vicious. And for those who can't dream of putting together the money to meet the price tag, there's always the prospect, however unlikely, of getting a job in one of the space hotels. How does that sound for a year working abroad?

| flight attendant | air steward or stewardess |
| skeptics / reservations | sceptics / bookings |

4.2

VOCABULARY
POSITIVE ADJECTIVES

2 Add vowels to complete the adjectives.

The ¹st_nn_ng Dingle Peninsula, sticking out into the Atlantic Ocean, is one of the most ²d_l_ghtf_l regions in Ireland. Only 199 miles from Dublin, it is famous for its ³s_gn_f_c_nt archaeological sites and is one of the least densely populated areas in the country. Castlegregory (population 205!), located on the north coast between Tralee and Dingle, is ⁴p_rf_ct for walking. You can also wander along the ⁵s_p_rb sandy beaches along the water's edge or explore the ⁶_xc_pt__n_l Maharee islands. Why not try the ⁷cl_ss_c walk up Mount Brandon, the second highest mountain in Ireland. From its summit, you can enjoy ⁸br__tht_k_ng views of the Blasket Islands, a tiny group of islands just off the coast. However, due to its closeness to the Atlantic, you might experience bad weather conditions since the weather can change suddenly, so make sure you're warmly dressed!

GRAMMAR
FUTURE FORMS

3 Correct the mistakes in the underlined phrases. One is correct.

A: Sue ¹<u>will take</u> a year off work, but she hasn't decided yet.

B: What ²<u>is she doing</u> if she does take the year off?

A: She said she ³<u>'s thinking to travel</u> a bit.

A: Look, they say there ⁴<u>'s likely to be</u> bad weather tomorrow.

B: I suppose they ⁵<u>'re postponing</u> the outdoor concert then.

A: Maybe. I ⁶<u>'m calling and asking</u> before we ⁷<u>'ll leave</u>.

A: Their boat ⁸<u>will get in</u> just after nine.

B: So when ⁹<u>are we going eating</u>?

A: After they ¹⁰<u>will arrive</u>, I guess.

4 Rewrite the sentences using the words in parentheses. Do not change the form of the word.

1 It will probably be hot tomorrow. (likely)
It _____

2 Chris wants to find a new job. (hoping)
Chris _____

3 I want to see Ingrid, and then I'll leave. (before)
I _____.

4 They're meeting at 3 o'clock tomorrow. (planning)
They _____

5 Barcelona is certain to win the championship. (definitely)
Barcelona _____.

6 Don't be late. We have to be at the theater at eight. (due)
Don't be late. We _____

7 There's a good chance that she'll get her work permit tomorrow. (likely)
She _____

8 I'm not likely to see you tomorrow. (probably)
I _____

VOCABULARY *PLUS*
UNCOUNTABLE AND PLURAL NOUNS

5 Complete the crossword.

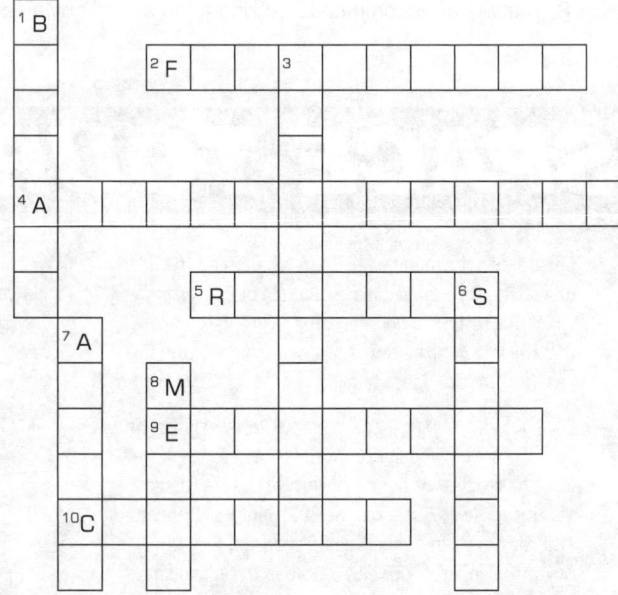

Across

2 a 4-star hotel has more of these and they're better
4 a place to sleep or stay for a while
5 what's left of an ancient building
9 e.g., in sports, a tennis racket, golf clubs
10 all the things in your bag

Down

1 suitcases
3 everything you find out when you ask questions
6 the view of natural features, for example out of a train window
7 suggestions
8 _____ of transportation

FUNCTION
DESCRIBING PROCEDURES

1 A Complete the rules for the game with the phrases in the box.

> what happens   after   way   the first thing   key thing
> the point   aim

Basically, the ¹_____ it works is that you draw a grid of 5x5 squares on a piece of paper. There are two players, and the ²_____ of the game is to complete the sequence "SOS" in a straight line as many times as you can. So ³_____ you do is one of you writes an "S" or an "O" in one of the squares. Then the other player writes an "S" or an "O" in another square.

Whenever one of you completes an "SOS", you get another turn, and ⁴_____ is not to let your partner succeed because ⁵_____ is that one player gets an "SOS" and then blocks the other player. It's easy to lose track of who's winning so the ⁶_____ is to keep score of who gets how many "SOSs". Then, ⁷_____ you've finished (once the grid is full), the winner is the player with the most "SOSs".

B Listen and check your answers.

VOCABULARY
ABILITIES

2 Find eight words or phrases for abilities in the wordsearch.

B	W	Y	W	E	R	A	T	I	N	V	E	W	F	H	J	K	L	A	S	I
K	A	G	O	O	D	S	E	N	S	E	O	F	H	U	M	O	R	U	P	N
M	G	W	F	D	S	H	M	L	K	J	P	M	N	E	R	T	I	N	G	G
N	G	F	B	L	S	A	W	Y	W	E	K	N	O	O	E	R	T	I	N	R
B	E	R	W	S	D	R	E	W	O	R	N	B	W	Y	W	E	R	T	I	E
F	R	W	E	R	T	P	G	T	C	O	O	L	H	E	A	D	E	D	Z	A
A	S	H	J	U	T	M	D	S	H	J	W	N	M	L	K	J	H	G	F	T
I	N	V	E	N	T	I	V	E	N	E	H	E	W	Y	W	E	R	T	I	S
Y	W	X	N	M	L	N	Y	P	S	R	O	V	E	W	U	L	D	S	H	H
F	H	R	G	O	O	D	W	I	T	H	W	O	R	D	S	P	K	X	S	A
J	G	K	F	H	J	K	L	H	S	D	F	G	H	J	S	R	W	E	R	P
U	N	D	E	R	S	T	A	N	D	H	U	M	A	N	N	A	T	U	R	E

3 Complete the sentences with the correct form of the words in Exercise 2.

1 You need to call an electrician. I can't fix the light, I don't have the _____.
2 I wouldn't tell Jeff any jokes, he doesn't have _____.
3 Hey Carol, you're _____. Have you been going to the gym?
4 That's a lovely poem, you're really _____.
5 Jake has a really bad temper, but Fatima is completely the opposite, she's very _____.
6 I'm not very _____. I could never write a book, for example.
7 Professor Cook has the _____ of anyone I've ever met. He can solve math problems really quickly.
8 If you feel upset, you should speak to Belinda. She _____, and she's a very good listener.

LEARN TO
USE MIRROR QUESTIONS

4 A Write mirror questions to check the words or phrases in italics.

1 A: Look up the idiom under the *key word*.
   B: Look up the idiom where?
2 A: You should see the *deputy director*.
   B: _____
3 A: I last spoke to her on *Christmas Eve*.
   B: _____
4 A: You can use a *question word* to clarify.
   B: _____
5 A: The *cast* is waiting backstage.
   B: _____
6 A: The rain's *lashing down*.
   B: _____
7 A: You'll find us in the *green room*.
   B: _____
8 A: The *podium* is too high.
   B: _____

B Listen and check your answers.

C Listen again and underline the main stressed word in each question.

D Listen and repeat, paying attention to the stress and intonation.

Look up the idiom where?

math / podium      maths / lectern

R2 REVIEW 2: UNITS 3–4

GRAMMAR NARRATIVE TENSES

1 Complete the story with the correct form of the verbs in parentheses. There may be more than one possibility.

It was May 1997, and I ¹_____ (think) it was going to be the last day of my life.
I ²_____ (study) archaeology in Greece with twelve other students for two months before that. We ³_____ (come) toward the end of our trip, there were only five days left, and that day we ⁴_____ (look) at the underwater ruins of an ancient town off the beach at Pavlopetri.
As I recall, the ruins were about 650 feet off the beach. It ⁵_____ (rain) the night before, and the water was still cool. Only half of us at a time ⁶_____ (swim) out to the ruins because we ⁷_____ (share) masks and snorkels, so we were taking turns to look at the ruins. After a while I ⁸_____ (begin) to feel tired and cold, so I ⁹_____ (tell) my friend Mike that I ¹⁰_____ (go) back to the beach. About halfway back to the beach, still in six-and-a-half-feet-deep water, I ¹¹_____ (realize) I was in trouble: I was very cold, I couldn't move my arms, and I ¹²_____ (go) in and out of consciousness. Fortunately, minutes earlier, Mike ¹³_____ (realize) that something was wrong. He was a qualified lifeguard, and he got me to the beach, but by then I ¹⁴_____ (shake) uncontrollably from hypothermia. Everyone ¹⁵_____ (massage) me to make me warm and only stopped when I ¹⁶_____ (recover).

VOCABULARY REVIEW

2 Complete the sentences with the correct word or phrase.

1 grew up/looked up to
  a) Gregor had always _____ his piano teacher.
  b) Jack _____ in a nice area of North London.
2 inspiring/hilarious
  a) I find the story of Nelson Mandela very _____.
  b) That comedian was really _____. I laughed all through the show.
3 stands for/pick up
  a) Danni has just started piano lessons. We're hoping he'll _____ it _____ OK.
  b) Our restaurant's name _____ good quality food.
4 taken on/brought up
  a) The company has _____ more than fifty new workers.
  b) We were _____ by our grandparents after our parents passed away.
5 switched off/focused on
  a) Eric wasn't interested in biology and _____ when the lecture started.
  b) Increasingly, Naomi _____ her work instead of all her other responsibilities.
6 burned up/chilled
  a) Ali was really _____ by his brother's comment.
  b) Sam _____ with his wife after a long day at work.
7 superb/breathtaking
  a) There are _____ views from the top of the hill.
  b) The Crown hotel is a _____ place for a relaxing weekend.
8 classic/significant
  a) The Jaguar e-type is a _____ car.
  b) The team made a _____ breakthrough in finding a cure for the illness.
9 stunning/perfect
  a) We want to find a house with a _____ view of the lake.
  b) This house is absolutely _____ for a professional couple like yourselves.

3 A Look at the underlined sounds in each group. Circle the words and phrases with the different sound.

1 b<u>i</u>ography, w<u>i</u>nd up, ch<u>i</u>ll
2 p<u>i</u>ck up, <u>i</u>nspiring, lyr<u>i</u>cs
3 br<u>ou</u>ght up, <u>au</u>tobiography, drop <u>ou</u>t
4 hilari<u>ou</u>s, foc<u>u</u>s on, grow <u>u</u>p
5 wikip<u>e</u>dia, r<u>e</u>charge, d<u>e</u>lightful
6 get <u>o</u>n, switch <u>o</u>ff, m<u>o</u>ving

B Listen and check. Then listen and repeat.

REVIEW 2: UNITS 3–4   R2

GRAMMAR I WISH, IF ONLY

4 Complete the underlined phrases.

What phone and Internet mistakes do you wish you could undo?

▶ ¹I wish / not post _____ a photo of myself in a swimsuit on a social networking site. When I went for an interview for a job, they'd attached it to my application form!

▶ I once emailed my first girlfriend when I was angry at my wife. ²I / really / wish / I / not _____. My wife found out, and she's never let me forget it.

▶ With hindsight, it was a bad idea to use the James Bond theme song for my ring tone. ³If / only / choose _____ something more sophisticated.

▶ I sent a joke text message to my boss. Thirty seconds after I'd sent it, I regretted it. ⁴If / only / send _____.
⁵Now / I / wish / I / delete _____ it.

▶ I recently joined a dating website and made the mistake of using a picture of myself from ten years ago. ⁶If only / I / have _____ all my hair again!

▶ I wrote a rude email to a friend, and I haven't heard from him since. I hope he emails me soon, or ⁷I / wish / he / phone / and / yell at / me _____. That would be better than waiting and wondering.

▶ An ex-boyfriend emailed me. Somehow I didn't get around to answering, and the next I heard he'd re-married. ⁸If only / I / reply _____ to his email, we might have gotten back together.

swimsuit / theme song swimming costume / theme tune

FUNCTION EXPRESSING LIKES AND DISLIKES

5 Complete the opinions with the words in the box.

| a | ~~into~~ | get | about | on | the | can't | what |

                       into
1 I couldn't get ∧ cooking with chilies. They're too spicy for my taste.
2 I hate steak when it's rare—I really don't like is the color.
3 What I like olives is their salty taste, particularly on pizzas.
4 I absolutely stand snails. The thought of them makes me feel sick.
5 I can't focus work right now. I'm completely exhausted.
6 I'm not big fan of cheese. There's something about the smell.
7 Cherries are my favorite fruit—thing I love about them is their taste.
8 I can't into chocolate because it's often too sweet for me.

GRAMMAR PRESENT AND PAST HABITS

6 Complete B's answers with the words in the box.

| didn't wasn't would (x2) ask weren't work to |

A: Do you mind people asking you about your childhood?
B: ¹No, I'm used it.
A: So, did you always want to be a singer?
B: Yes. ²From the age of four, I dress up and sing for my parents.
A: But after their divorce, you were brought up by your grandparents?
B: ³That's right, but they used to having children around, so I was sent away to school, which I hated. ⁴I used to sitting still for so long.
A: But you did well in the end, didn't you?
B: Yes, eventually. ⁵I used to the teacher what she wanted me to do, and I also worked very hard.
A: Did anyone recognize your talent at that point?
B: ⁶No, I use to enjoy the music classes, so I hardly ever joined in. But then we got a new teacher. ⁷He used to for a music publisher, and he put my song "Sampling Love" on the Internet.
A: And as they say, the rest is history.
B: ⁸Yes, I often think about being a famous singer, and now it's happened.

REVIEW 2: UNITS 3–4

GRAMMAR FUTURE FORMS

7 Complete the articles with an appropriate future form of the verbs in the boxes. There may be more than one possibility.

`use   become   be likely   think`

All charged up?

¹_____ you _____ of buying an electric car but are worried about the amount of time it takes to charge the batteries? All that ²_____ to change thanks to a discovery by scientists in the USA. The new batteries ³_____ lithium iron phosphate and ⁴_____ available within two years.

`continue   not keep   lose   break`

THIS YEAR ... OR MAYBE NEXT?

Happy New Year! Now the bad news: three out of four of us ⁵_____ our New Year resolutions by the end of January. Even worse, a quarter of us ⁶_____ our promises until the end of week one. "People's intentions are always good," says the manager of a nation-wide chain of gyms. "They say they ⁷_____ weight and get fit. But ⁸_____ they _____ when it gets difficult? No, they give up."

`have   ask   talk   meet`

Personal Vacation Planner

We ⁹_____ at 6 o'clock for a twenty-minute talk with out personal vacation planner. We ¹⁰_____ about vacation destinations. I'm ¹¹_____ him about two or three places I've always wanted to visit, like Sweden or Lapland, and my partner wants to ask him about Panama and Costa Rica. I think he ¹²_____ a very difficult time getting me and my partner to agree.

VOCABULARY PLUS UNCOUNTABLE AND PLURAL NOUNS

8 Add -s in eight places and remove it from five places. Make any other necessary changes to the spelling.

TRAVEL

There is a maximum weight of forty-four pounds for passengers' baggages. Security is strict at the airport, and you will be asked to confirm that no one has interfered with the content of your bags. The airport is situated on the outskirt of the city, and there are several mean of transportations to get downtown. We recommend the airport bus because it is cheaper and more reliable than the taxis. Full informations about your accommodations can be found on our website. Note that all hotels are three-star and have facility such as laundry, TV in every room, and Internet access. Electricities voltage is 220V, and you will need an adaptor or European plug.

TOURS

Tours are available daily and include a visit to the remain of the old city a few miles to the north and a visit to the desert in the south, with stunning view from the bus of the spectacular sceneries. There will be an opportunity to meet some of the local and buy their handmade goods. We will also visit the approximate site of the tombs of the kings, although their exact whereabout are not known.

FUNCTION DESCRIBING PROCEDURES

9 Correct the mistakes in the underlined phrases.

A great steak makes a quick, tasty meal but is hard to get right. ¹The first thing you do is making sure the steak is the right temperature. If it is frozen, then defrost it overnight. ²A point is to make sure the meat is at room temperature so that it cooks well throughout.

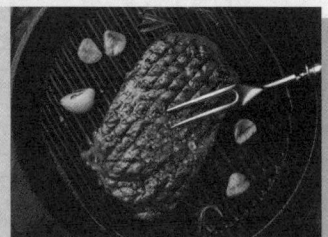

Next, pre-heat a heavy griddle pan over a high heat. ³Key thing is to ensure the pan is sufficiently hot, but not smoking, or the steak will be cooked unevenly. Meanwhile season the meat and brush it with a little oil. Put the meat in the pan and, after you've cooked one side, turn it over. ⁴What you has to do is keep turning it or it can dry out.

⁵Basic, the way it works is that the meat is full of flavor, so never cut it to check if it's cooked. Right at the end, press the steak gently with your finger: rare should be soft, well done firm and medium in between. ⁶After you've remove the steak from the pan, cover it with foil and "rest" it for a few minutes, then the juices can run back through the steak. ⁷What it happens next is up to you. You can serve it with potatoes or salad or accompany it with a sauce. Enjoy!

flavor — flavour

REVIEW 2: UNITS 3–4   R2

CHECK

Circle the correct option to complete the sentences.

1. When I was young, I _____ I could do anything.
   a) used to believe   b) would believe
   c) 'm used to believing

2. Have you read the new _____? It was written by his ex-wife.
   a) gossip   b) biography   c) autobiography

3. Do you ever wish you _____ back in time?
   a) would go   b) went   c) could go

4. Neil never gets angry with people, he's very _____.
   a) cool headed   b) good with words   c) inventive

5. If only I _____ my flared pants—they're back in fashion now.
   a) hadn't thrown away   b) could keep
   c) didn't throw away

6. Are you used _____ spicy food?
   a) eat   b) to eat   c) to eating

7. Look, _____ the game, and you might win it.
   a) focus on   b) recharge   c) burn up

8. Jason and Zena _____ together again after their very public argument.
   a) won't probably work   b) probably won't work
   c) won't work probably

9. First _____ the leaflet, then you can stop for a coffee.
   a) you will finish   b) you to finish
   c) you are finishing

10. We're getting worried because they haven't _____ the present yet, and it's nearly Lisa's birthday.
    a) brought up   b) picked up   c) take on

11. Then _____ that microwaves cause the food to vibrate quickly and produce heat.
    a) the thing happens   b) the thing is
    c) what happens is

12. They _____ living with the constant heat.
    a) wouldn't   b) weren't used to   c) didn't use to

13. _____ the picture, you can adjust it on your computer.
    a) After you've taken   b) After that you've taken
    c) After that you take

14. Have you found all of the missing _____?
    a) remain   b) equipment   c) outskirts

15. I _____ the job because I'm interested in working with animals.
    a) passed away   b) stood for   c) took on

16. You can get _____ views from the summit of the mountain.
    a) exceptional   b) significant   c) poignant

17. The special effects are so _____ you almost feel that you're in space too.
    a) moving   b) incredible   c) hilarious

18. Stop complaining and just _____ with the job!
    a) look up to   b) get by   c) get on

19. They _____ the house for an hour when it started raining.
    a) painted   b) had painted   c) had been painting

20. Neela felt relieved because she _____ the speech and could send it off to be checked.
    a) was writing   b) 'd written   c) 'd been writing

21. _____ move your money to another bank?
    a) Are you thinking   b) Are you hoping
    c) Are you planning to

22. What lovely flowers! _____ you had bought some for me, too!
    a) I didn't wish   b) If only   c) Couldn't have

23. In the event of a leak, call a plumber—you don't have the _____ to stop the water going everywhere.
    a) know-how   b) sharp mind   c) sense of humor

24. I'd get her some flowers. She's _____ chocolates.
    a) couldn't get into   b) not a big fan of
    c) can't stand

25. What _____ around.
    a) goes around comes   b) bitten around shy
    c) a cloud around a silver lining

26. _____ shy.
    a) Once bitten, twice   b) When bitten, always
    c) Once bitten, always

27. The hotel is situated in a _____ location, right next to the sea.
    a) classic   b) significant   c) stunning

28. I can't put this lawnmower together. Where's the _____?
    a) manual   b) wikipedia   c) manga

29. _____ I like about the color is it's so vibrant.
    a) The thing what   b) What   c) It's what

30. How many actors _____ before you chose Rob?
    a) had you seen   b) had you been seeing?
    c) were you seeing

RESULTS /30

pants / argument   trousers / row

5.1

LISTENING

1 A Listen to the radio program about the Ig Nobel Prize and number the pictures in the order they are mentioned.

A ☐   B ☐   C ☐

D ☐

B Listen again and complete the descriptions of other Ig Nobel winners.

1 Research into why pregnant women don't _____ over.
2 Research into why dry spaghetti breaks into _____ pieces.
3 A device that makes an annoying noise that only _____ can hear.
4 A business suit that automatically _____ itself.
5 A washing machine for _____ and _____.

C Listen again and circle the best ending, a), b) or c).

1 The name "Ig Nobel" suggests:
   a) a link to the Nobel prize.
   b) that the prize is "ignoble" or stupid.
   c) two meanings at the same time.
2 It is awarded for:
   a) ridiculous research and inventions.
   b) amusing but interesting inventions.
   c) potentially major research.
3 The alarm clock was awarded an Ig Nobel prize because:
   a) it was good for the economy.
   b) it helped people get up.
   c) it meant people worked harder.
4 Martha is doing research into:
   a) how to stay dry in the rain.
   b) how people get wet in the rain.
   c) whether an umbrella or a raincoat is better in the rain.

VOCABULARY

CHANGE

2 A Underline the correct words to complete the sentences.

1 John was finding it hard to adapt *to/at* the weather in the new country.
2 Small amounts of radiation can have a positive effect *on/to* some cancer patients.
3 Artificial intelligence will *transform/enable* the way we live.
4 I can't believe you hit my car. You've caused a lot of damage *to/at* the back of it.
5 It wasn't easy to adjust *at/to* life at college.
6 Taking drugs can have devastating effects *on/with* people's lives.
7 That bad publicity did a lot of harm *to/for* our sales.
8 Putting classes online has enabled people to *access/accept* learning when and where they want.
9 We have to *revolutionize/criticize* the way we produce energy—we can't rely on fossil fuels forever.

B Listen and write the words and phrases next to the correct stress pattern.

| adjust to   damage   access   transform   effect |
| revolutionize   devastating   positive   enable |
| do harm to   adapt to |

Oo   _____   _____
oO   _____   _____
ooOoo   _____
Oooo   _____
oOo   _____   _____
          _____   _____
Ooo   _____

C Listen again and repeat.

GRAMMAR
ARTICLES

3 Complete the article with *a(n)*, *the* or – (no article).

AN INVENTOR OR THE INVENTOR?

It's ¹_____ well-known fact that ²_____ electric light was invented by Thomas Edison, but is it really true? Edison's light bulb, like many inventions, was ³_____ result of many scientists' work. ⁴_____ English scientist had made ⁵_____ simple electric light seventy years earlier, and Edison's further development of ⁶_____ idea wouldn't have been possible without the work of his colleagues.

Similarly, the Wright brothers are generally credited with inventing the first successful airplane at ⁷_____ beginning of ⁸_____ twentieth century. Yet literally dozens of ⁹_____ inventors and scientists before that time might claim to have taken key steps in developing ¹⁰_____ sustained flight. For instance, ¹¹_____ Norwegian named Navrestad supposedly flew in a glider in 1825 and, in subsequent years, ¹²_____ advances were made all over the world. In fact, just before the Wright brothers' famous flight, ¹³_____ American named Langley flew over ¹⁴_____ Potomac River, a distance of about 2600 feet.

It seems that ¹⁵_____ person who not only achieves a particular feat but also records it, protects it and publicizes it will be credited with the discovery.

4 Read the article. Cross out *the* in ten places where it is unnecessary.

YOUR MILLION-DOLLAR IDEA

Do you want to join those people who have made a million from a simple idea? Then just follow these five tips:

💰 Remember the saying "necessity is the mother of the invention." When the people need the things, sooner or later someone will come up with an idea to meet that need. It could be you!

💰 Watch people and notice their habits. How do they do the everyday activities, such as answering the phone, handling the money or the credit cards, eating and drinking? Is there a way that one of the activities could be made easier?

💰 When you have an idea, write it down. Draw a picture. Give it a name. This will help your mind work on the idea further.

💰 Don't talk to the negative people about your ideas. The motivation is important for the creativity and negative people can kill it.

💰 Talk to a friend about your ideas. Some of the most successful ideas emerge through the talking.

VOCABULARY PLUS
COMPOUND NOUNS

5 Complete the compound nouns with the words in the box.

> through   off   look   back   down   come   side

1 Cell phone access is possible almost everywhere, but the down_____ is the increasing number of ugly antennas.

2 One positive out_____ of the availability of electronic media is a decrease in the amount of paper used.

3 The transistor was a major break_____ in the development of electronic devices.

4 In the early days of cell phones, there was a trade-_____ between battery size and compactness.

5 The biggest draw_____ of the development of electronic communication has been that people see less of each other in person.

6 After the development of atomic weapons, the out_____ for human warfare became depressing and frightening.

7 The use of automated telephone response systems often leads to a communication break_____ between customers and providers.

publicizes   publicises

1 A Look at the words in the box. Which do you think are the five best words (B) and which are the five worst words (W) to use in an advertisement?

> Safety   Deal   Quality   Results   Love
> Client   Discover   Cheap   Health   Best

B Read the article and complete it with the words in the box above.

THE TEN BEST AND WORST WORDS IN ADVERTISING

Everyone likes to get something for nothing, but the word "free" has become **a big no-no** because it's sure to make people think of a product as second-rate. What are the words that are guaranteed to get results? And what words should advertisers avoid using? Check out the five power words in advertising and five others that advertisers should delete from their lexicons.

☺ THE TOP FIVE

¹_____—Everybody wants it, everybody needs it, and it's so hard to get. Just the mention of it catches people's attention and makes them want the product that seems to promise to deliver.

²_____—There's a bit of the explorer in all of us, and, while most people are **armchair explorers**, the sense that they are going to experience something new is irresistible.

³_____—This has always been important to consumers, but we've seen a clear trend since the 1980s to put physical and mental well-being **at the forefront**. Most people are too busy or too lazy to pay attention to their own, and that's all the more reason to make them buy some via your product.

⁴_____—Just a mild suggestion that a product will keep the consumer's family out of danger–particularly if the advertiser can associate the product with protecting children–and most consumers will **dig deeper into their pockets** to pay out.

⁵_____—One advertising psychologist has said that the power of this word is in the association consumers make with their childhood and school; getting good grades was the goal then, and this word makes them think of that. And yes, they still want good ones.

☹ THE BOTTOM FIVE

⁶_____—Most people will **go to great lengths** to pay less for a product, but this is probably the worst word to communicate that that's what you offer. When it refers to price, it makes the product sound second-rate; unluckily, the word can also refer to quality.

⁷_____—Sure, it's OK to talk about the customer or consumer using this word, but consumers don't like to be referred to in such a technical, business-orientated way.

⁸_____—Similar to "cheap," this word has associations with tricky used-car salesmen and products that aren't in fact worth spending money on.

⁹_____—Only one product can really be described with this word, and, if everyone says theirs is, then who should the consumer believe?

¹⁰_____—Another word that was once very much in fashion, but overuse has **made consumers numb to** its meaning. And who would say their product doesn't have it?

2 Match the meanings 1–6 with the phrases in bold in the article.

1 make extra effort for something you want badly _____
2 people who dream about doing something, but don't actually do it _____
3 try hard(er) to get money for something _____
4 something you should never do _____
5 a top priority _____
6 cause people not even to notice _____

VOCABULARY
ADVERTISING COLLOCATIONS

3 Complete the sentences. The first letter of each word is given.

1 We're l_____ our new product next month at the trade exhibition.
2 We e_____ the market with a new product.
3 Let's r_____ the price so more people can afford our goods.
4 Apple d_____ the smartphone market.
5 The technology company b_____ into the fashion market with smart clothes.
6 We've just decided on the price. We s_____ it so that it's similar to the competition.
7 We sponsor a lot of sporting events to p_____ our brand name.
8 The price of bread has i_____ by twenty-five percent recently.
9 When a celebrity says a product is good, they e_____ the product.
10 Sofex r_____ the price of their new colorful tablet—they are so popular people will pay more for them.
11 The new brand will be a_____ on TV, the Internet and radio.
12 Our researchers can see a g_____ in the market.

GRAMMAR
REAL AND HYPOTHETICAL CONDITIONALS

4 Complete the second sentence so that it has a similar meaning to the first. Use between two and five words including the word given.

1 Without increasing the budget, we can't put an ad on TV.   UNLESS
We can't put an ad on TV _____ the budget.

2 Not many people use the store because it closes at five o'clock.   LATER
If the store _____, more people would use it.

3 Could we get a discount by paying in cash?   SUPPOSING
_____ in cash, could we get a discount?

4 Providing we're happy with your work, we'll give you a full-time contract.   LONG
We'll give you a full-time contract _____ happy with your work.

5 Suppose I accepted the job, how soon would you want me to start?   WERE
If I _____ the job, how soon would you want me to start?

6 Supposing you don't get the job, what would you do then?   LET'S
_____ you don't get the job, what would you do then?

5 Complete the sentences with the appropriate form of the verbs in parentheses.

1 If the store _____ (not have) the right version, I _____ (definitely/get) it online.

2 If I _____ (not be) left-handed, I _____ (not wear) my watch on my right wrist.

3 We _____ (close) the factory unless a buyer _____ (come forward) in the next few days.

4 If Cindy _____ (not be) at the party now, you _____ (be) miserable.

5 If I _____ (not sit) here now, I _____ (be) at home playing the guitar.

6 I _____ (buy) you dinner provided that we _____ (pass) the exam!

WRITING
A REPORT; LEARN TO MAKE WRITTEN COMPARISONS

6 A Put the words in the correct order to make phrases.

a) for / less / is / important / far
_____

b) contrast / an / to / show / interesting
_____

c) on / place / importance / greater
_____

d) is / in / no / there / difference / almost
_____

e) equally / both / more / less / affects / groups / or
_____

f) differences / significant / are / there / in
_____

g) a / shows / slight / only / variation
_____

B Look at the chart and complete the sentences with the phrases from Exercise 6A.

1 Looking at men and women in the younger age group, the way the glasses look _____.

2 _____ the number of people who don't have an upgradable TV.

3 Comparing younger men and women, the importance of price and image quality _____.

4 _____ the number of people who watch action movies—the movies that benefit the most from the 3D effect.

5 Younger men _____ how trendy 3D TV is than the other groups.

6 The results for the older groups _____ those for the younger group.

7 The way the glasses look _____ people in the older age group than the 18-to-25-year-olds.

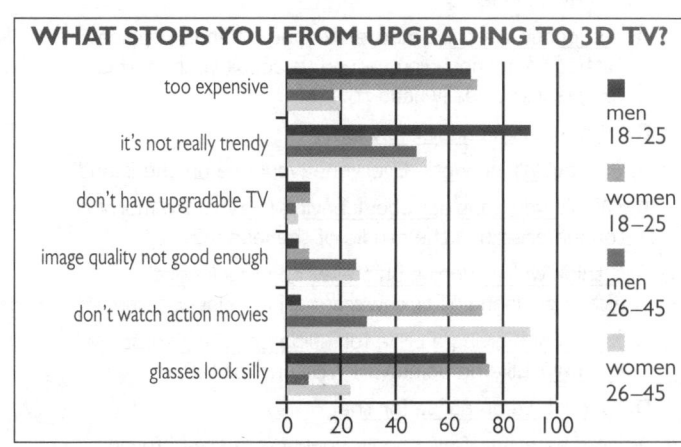

C Write five more sentences about the data in the chart.

FUNCTION
SUGGESTING IDEAS

1 A Read the list of ideas. Which two do you think would be the best in your situation?

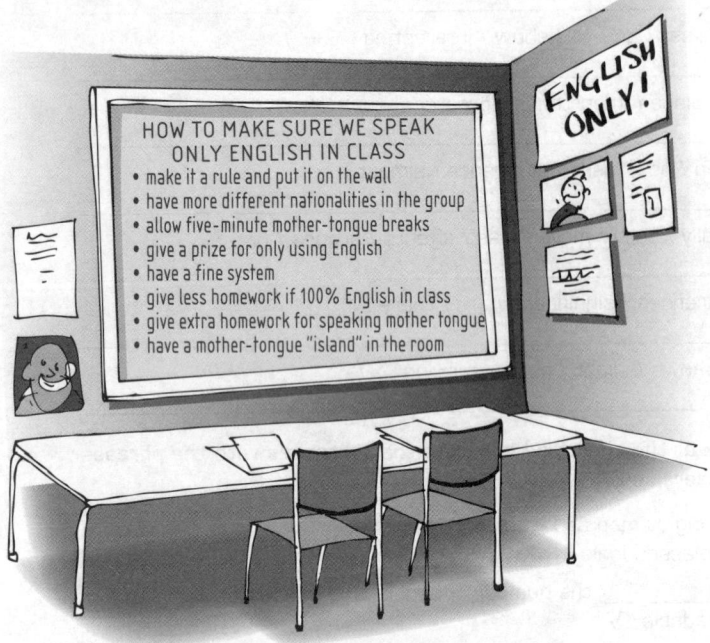

HOW TO MAKE SURE WE SPEAK ONLY ENGLISH IN CLASS
- make it a rule and put it on the wall
- have more different nationalities in the group
- allow five-minute mother-tongue breaks
- give a prize for only using English
- have a fine system
- give less homework if 100% English in class
- give extra homework for speaking mother tongue
- have a mother-tongue "island" in the room

B Read the conversation. Do the speakers share your ideas?

A: What do you think about simply writing the rule on a sign on the wall: "English only"?

B: I think it's too simple. We'd ignore it.

C: [1]<u>How much do you feel about a fine system?</u> You have to pay if you speak your language.

B: [2]<u>That could be a problem idea.</u> Not everyone has money for fines.

A: [3]<u>I suppose we try</u> a mother-tongue "island." A place in the room where you can go to speak your mother tongue if you really need to.

C: [4]<u>That's not a bad terribly idea.</u>

B: [5]<u>It wouldn't be work.</u> Everyone would be on the island!

A: [6]<u>Would you consider about having</u> five-minute mother-tongue breaks in the middle of the lesson?

B: [7]<u>I think we're running on the wrong track here.</u> It's either punishment or reward, nothing else works.

C: [8]<u>How does giving a prize for using only English strike you out?</u> Like no homework? Or chocolate?

B: [9]<u>Should we go agree for that?</u>

A: [10]<u>It'd be great if we should could get</u> more different nationalities in the group. Then we'd naturally speak English more.

B: [11]<u>It wouldn't be my first last choice.</u> Where are we going to find these people?

C: [12]<u>I'm torn up between punishment and reward systems.</u> Fines or prizes.

A: Could we go for both?

B: Yeah, [13]<u>let's go out with that.</u>

C Cross out the unnecessary word in each underlined phrase.

D Listen to the conversation or read the audio script on pages 77–78 to check.

VOCABULARY
COLLOCATIONS WITH *IDEA*

2 A Complete the words by adding vowels.

1 People who read that won't understand it, the ideas are much too **b_z_rr_**.

2 When the movie started, I already knew how it was going to end. The idea for the movie was very **pr_d_ct_bl_**.

3 They both refused to speak until the other apologized for **cr_t_c_z_ng** their ideas.

4 Harry's just started, at the bank and thinks he'll be running it within a year. He's already **c_m_ng _p w_th** ideas for how to change things.

5 The directors **r_j_ct_d** her idea for expanding the business because they thought it was too risky.

6 Have you heard? The director wants to fire Sophie for having that **dr_ _df_l** idea—it cost the company thousands of dollars.

7 So you want to drive 1250 miles in two days, all by yourself? I think that's an **_nr_ _l_st_c** idea.

8 That's the best idea I've ever heard! It's **br_ll_ _nt**.

B Listen to the words and circle the correct stress pattern.

1 OooO		5 Ooo	oOo
2 oOoo	ooOo	6 OooO	
3 Oooo	ooOo	7 oOoo	ooOo
4 Oooo	ooOo	8 OooO	

LEARN TO
SHOW RESERVATIONS

3 A Correct the mistake in each sentence.

1 To be honestly, I thought your first suggestion was better.

2 To put bluntly, that's the worst idea I've heard today.

3 Actual, I don't think that's a very practical idea.

4 Frankedly, it's just not going to work.

5 I have to saying, that's probably the only way.

B Listen and check. Then listen again and repeat, paying attention to the stress and intonation.

VOCABULARY
AGE

1 A Correct B's sentences by changing one word.

1. **A:** I'm going to play on the swings …
   B: Behave your age! They're meant for kids.
2. **A:** Mina seems very sensible for a sixteen-year-old.
   B: I'm continually surprised by her maternity.
3. **A:** I can't believe he's seventy!
   B: Yes, he looks very young than his age.
4. **A:** What are you doing this weekend?
   B: We're visiting an elder aunt of Simon's.
5. **A:** I think Hugh is too young to become a manager.
   B: Careful—that could be seen as age judgment.
6. **A:** In her forties, Madonna is attracting even more crowds.
   B: Yes, she's definitely in her time.
7. **A:** You could say that social networking sites have "grown up."
   B: I agree—they've certainly reached of age now.
8. **A:** I can't believe what he just said!
   B: Yeah, he's so unmature. He really needs to grow up.

B Are the age-related phrases in B's responses positive (+), negative (-) or neutral (N)?

GRAMMAR
MODAL VERBS AND RELATED PHRASES

2 Complete the article with the words and phrases in the box. You do not need to use one of the words or phrases.

> can   could   are able   being able to   managed to   couldn't
> should   had to   don't have to   are supposed to   made
> wasn't allowed   let

WHAT WAS LIFE LIKE BEFORE THE INTERNET?

- If you wanted to keep in touch with friends, you ¹_____ just visit a social networking site. You ²_____ phone or talk to friends face to face.

- To sell something, you paid for an ad in the local paper. These days you ³_____ to reach thousands of potential buyers through sites such as Craigslist or eBay. Before you buy, you ⁴_____ read the conditions thoroughly. If someone else is bidding for you, don't ⁵_____ them bid without giving them a limit.

- Online encyclopedias didn't exist. As a student, once I only ⁶_____ find information for an assignment by spending two days in a library.

- Music came from stores in the form of CDs. Nowadays it ⁷_____ be downloaded online. Obviously a good thing? Well, you ⁸_____ pay for, but many people download illegally.

- Before life online, as a kid I was ⁹_____ to write long thank-you letters for birthday presents instead of ¹⁰_____ send a quick email. My parents were really strict. I ¹¹_____ to play with any new toys until I'd written to everyone.

- You used to go to friends' homes to watch their vacation videos. Thankfully, you ¹²_____ do this anymore. A quick look on a video-sharing site is enough!

3 Complete the second sentence so that it has a similar meaning to the first. Use between two and five words including the word given.

1. There's no obligation for the company to provide training.   HAVE
   The company _____ training.
2. It's impossible to force kids to eat vegetables.   MAKE
   You _____ vegetables.
3. We weren't able to see the supervisor.   MANAGE
   We _____ see the supervisor.
4. He was allowed to go after he'd been questioned for three hours.   LET
   The police _____ after he'd been questioned for three hours.
5. I'm afraid I can't make the meeting.   ABLE
   I'm afraid I _____ make the meeting.
6. This area is forbidden. Get out immediately.   SUPPOSED
   You _____ in this area. Get out immediately.

6.1

6 age

37

6.1

LISTENING

4 A How would you answer questions 1–8?

WHAT'S THE BEST AGE...

1 to choose a career?
2 to get married?
3 to have a baby?
4 to start a sport?
5 to learn a musical instrument?
6 to learn a new language?
7 to become president or prime minister?
8 to retire?

B Listen to four speakers. Which question above does each person answer?

Speaker 1: _____
Speaker 2: _____
Speaker 3: _____
Speaker 4: _____

C Listen again and answer the questions.

Speaker 1
1 What age does the speaker think is best?
2 What three factors are important?

Speaker 2
3 What does the speaker think the minimum and maximum age should be?
4 What two factors need to be balanced?

Speaker 3
5 Why do you need to understand yourself and your relationship?
6 What is the wrong age, according to the speaker?

Speaker 4
7 When does the speaker think it's OK for a young person to make a choice?
8 What advice does the speaker give to other people?

D Match the phrases in bold with the meanings a)–e).

1 I don't think there's any **hard and fast** rule.
2 She's **still going strong** now she's over seventy.
3 You have to **strike a balance** between maturity and energy.
4 It **has to do with** giving yourself enough time to get to know yourself.
5 That **worked for** me.

a) was successful
b) choose a moderate way, compromise
c) fixed, definite
d) is connected to
e) continuing to be successful

VOCABULARY *PLUS*
WORD-BUILDING: PREFIXES

5 A Put the words in the correct group according to the negative prefix they take.

| realistic satisfied behave secure familiar |
| predictable logical patient mortal willing |
| interpret relevant healthy |

1 un: _____ _____ _____
   _____ _____
2 im: _____ _____ _____
3 mis: _____ _____
4 il: _____
5 ir: _____
6 dis: _____
7 in: _____

B Complete the text with the negative form of words in Exercise 5A. You do not need three of the words.

Dealing with Difficult Students

Students are motivated to learn by a variety of factors. Some look for a sense of personal achievement, while others enjoy being involved as a member of a learning group.

Teachers sometimes make the mistake of having [1]_____ expectations of students. It is better to be patient with their progress rather than being [2]_____ because being [3]_____ to let students learn from their own mistakes can be demotivating.

Students often have a lot to deal with, particularly if they are moving from an environment they know to an [4]_____ learning environment. They may feel unsure and [5]_____ because they are not used to the new systems and may become [6]_____ with their new school and way of life. These feelings can take many forms of expression, such as sadness or attention-seeking and a tendency to [7]_____.

Whatever form of behavior this takes, the teacher can show understanding by responding to students using expressions such as "I understand why you feel like that, but ...." The teacher should pay attention to what the student is really saying, even if it sometimes seems to be [8]_____ and unconnected to the subject.

It is easy to [9]_____ the new students' actions and statements, so it is important to keep listening and communicating with them and letting them know that you are there to support them and not simply to judge them. Start by telling them this and your relationship will soon change from an [10]_____ and harmful one into one that is happy and motivating.

C Write the negative form of words in Exercise 5A in the correct group according to the stress pattern.

oooOo _____
ooOoo _____ _____
oOoo _____ _____ _____
oOo _____ _____ _____
_____
ooO _____
ooOo _____

D Listen and check. Then listen and repeat.

READING

1 A Read the article. Which of the following topics are not mentioned?

> work   transportation   clothes   food   relationships   shopping
> energy   social networking   newspapers   radio and television

B Six sentences have been removed from the article. Complete the article with sentences a)–f).

a) Work comes to you.
b) Now the restaurant's bioprinter starts to produce the raw ingredients for the restaurant AIPA to cook and bring to the table.
c) Some do accounting, some write letters.
d) You have instant video chat, Internet browsing and can do many other things you needed a smartphone for previously.
e) You control what happens in the whole house from here, so you remotely switch on the lights and the shower and tell the kitchen you'll be ready for breakfast in 20 minutes.
f) Computers inside your car take away the need for manual driving.

C Read the article again. Are the statements true (T), false (F) or is the information not given (NG)?

1 You are woken up early because of an important news bulletin.
2 Your artificially intelligent personal assistant has checked your health.
3 Your clothes are newly made as soon as you have decided what to wear.
4 Cars are designed to be energy efficient.
5 The ingredients for your food are produced at the restaurant by a bioprinter.
6 Flying machines make deliveries to your home.
7 Smart glasses save everything you do during the day so that you can play it back later.
8 Your own home contributes fifteen per cent of the electricity you use.

2030 VISION

Smartphones are museum pieces and cable TV—well what was that? The world will be very different in the future, but what will everyday life be like in 2030?

06:45
You're gently woken up in your sleep pod—you don't sleep in a bed, they've developed dramatically into sleep pods. ¹_____ Meanwhile your artificially intelligent personal assistant (AIPA) has started work monitoring your body functions and making sure you're fit and well for the day ahead.

07:50
You're ready for work, but you don't need to go anywhere. ²_____ You enter your virtual office and greet co-workers from around the world in your virtual work environment. You and your colleague in Singapore look at the live data feeds and make real-time decisions about your work. Then a co-worker nearby asks for a face-to-face meeting over lunch. You decide what to wear, and an army of nanobots make the clothes for you.

12:30
Your journey is still by car—but you don't drive it. It drives. ³_____ They talk to the smart road that is regulating the flow of traffic so that cars are traveling at maximum speed and efficiency. You know there won't be a delay because of a car accident—there hasn't been a car crash for ten years now.

12.45
You arrive for your meal. Your car has already suggested a menu—beef goulash. ⁴_____ During the meal, your co-worker mentions her new smart glasses, and this reminds you that a drone will deliver yours later today.

15:30
Work's finished. You have a lot more leisure time now because AIPAs can do a lot of the work for us and a lot quicker. ⁵_____ Not all AIPA's have human form, some are simply computer programs with human-like intelligence and understanding. Right on time, the drone arrives with your smart glasses.

19:00
In the evening, you see what your new smart glasses can do. Smart glasses have replaced the smartphone because they are a lot easier to use and have a lot more functions. ⁶_____ Even better, they record every minute of your day for you so that you can watch your day again—speeded up this time.

22:00
As you sleep, the smart electricity grid and your smart electrical appliances are saving electricity and sending it to where it is needed most. In fact, it has been doing this 24/7, but at night it becomes very noticeable as your fridge powers down and the street lights dim. We can finally see the stars from our cities again.

6.2

GRAMMAR
FUTURE PERFECT AND CONTINUOUS

2 Underline the correct alternative.

1 Nine o'clock's too late to arrive. The concert *will start/will be starting/will have started* by then.

2 You can use my desk. I *won't use/won't be using/won't have used* it tomorrow because I'm away.

3 Dr. Sawali will be happy to lead a discussion during the conference because she *'ll attend/'ll be attending/'ll have attended* it anyway.

4 Will you still *need/be needing/have needed* me when I'm sixty-four?

5 Your two-day visit *will involve/will be involving/will have involved* a factory tour and several meetings.

6 By this time tomorrow, the championship draw *will happen/will be happening/will have happened*, and we'll know who we're playing.

3 A Complete the predictions made in the 1950s about life in 2020. Use the future perfect or future continuous.

1 The world / experience / mini ice-age / at that time.
The world will be experiencing a mini ice-age at that time.

2 The average weight / adult male / go down / to fifty pounds.
_____

3 Smoking / ban / completely / in all public areas.
_____

4 Everyone / drive / flying cars.
_____

5 Men and women / wear / same clothes.
_____

6 Poverty and famine / halve.
_____

B Which predictions above have already come true (✓), which may well come true (?) and which are unlikely to come true (✗)?

VOCABULARY
OPTIMISM/PESSIMISM

4 Write letters to complete the words.

1 feel good about a future event
= look _ _ _ _ _ _ _ _ _ _

2 have good and bad experiences
= have u_ _ _ _ _ _ _ _ _ _ _ _ _

3 make no progress = _ _ _ _ _ _ _ _ _ _ _ _

4 have emotions which are both positive and negative
= have m_ _ _ _ _ f_ _ _ _ _ _ _ _

5 see the positive side of things
= _ _ _ _ _ _ _ _ _ _ _ _ _ _ _ _ _ side

6 positive = up_ _ _ _ _

7 fear = dr_ _ _ _

8 create a feeling of hopelessness
= fill with de_ _ _ _ _ _

WRITING
AN INFORMAL EMAIL; LEARN TO FOCUS ON INFORMAL STYLE

5 A Complete the sentences with the words in the box.

| for   all   about   to   know   rather   get   'd   let   be |

1 April is *a great time* _____ visiting Budapest— the spring festival is on.

2 Now, _____ your idea of traveling to New York. I _____ love to come along.

3 Sheila was *happy to* _____ an email from her friend in Indonesia.

4 It'd _____ great if we could get free tickets to the concert. I'll _____ *you know* when it starts.

5 I'm really excited about planning our vacation together, *I can't wait* _____ meet again and plan it in more detail. See you again soon. _____ *the best!*

6 *Do you* _____ which is the closest airport to Brighton? *I'd* _____ land as near to the city as possible.

B Complete the emails words and phrases in *italics* from Exercise 5A

Hi Levent!
I was really ¹_____ your text. I can't believe you're finally coming to Liverpool! I knew the information ²_____ the music festival, in fact I was planning to go myself. If you're going, too, why don't we go together? It'd ³_____ to hang out for a while. In fact, you could come earlier and stay with us for a few days. You always said you'd like to spend some time in the city, and this would be ⁴_____ it. What do you know about Liverpool – ⁵_____ what you'd like to see?
⁶_____,
Tim

Hello Tim,
What a surprise that you're going, too!
⁷_____ to see you and your family, but it's difficult to visit you before the festival—⁸_____ come after, if that's OK. Do you have any details about the festival? Can you send them to me? I'll ⁹_____ what my plans are next week. ¹⁰_____ hear more about the festival.
All the best,
Levent

VOCABULARY
COLLOCATIONS

1 A Complete the questions with the correct collocations.

1. How long have you had your current cr_____ ca_____?
2. Do you mind st_____ home al_____?
3. Have you ever ri_____ a sc_____? If not, would you like to?
4. Do you think it's OK for men to we_____ make-up?
5. How la_____ do you think parents should let children st_____ up?
6. Have you ever ru_____ your own bu_____? If not, would you enjoy it?
7. How many smartphones have you ow_____?
8. How many so_____ ne_____ websites have you used, if any?
9. Have you ever done a pa_____-ti_____ job?
10. Would you feel safe tr_____ so_____ around another country?
11. When you were younger did you ever ba_____ for a toddler?
12. Should children be allowed to get their ears pi_____?

B Answer each question using no more than three words.

FUNCTION
PERSUADING

2 A Correct the mistakes in A's sentences.

1. **A:** Look at this picture. Isn't that it time they banned "size zero" models?
   B: Well, clothes do look pretty good on them.
   A: But it sends a terrible message to young girls. Shouldn't they be knowing it isn't normal to be so skinny?
   B: I've never really thought about it much.
   A: Well, you should. Clearly so, these images add to the pressure on young girls.
   B: Yeah, you're probably right.

2. **A:** Aren't you thinking that they should use technology in football games?
   B: What, you mean instead of referees?
   A: Yeah, to make decisions. No one can't see it would be fairer.
   B: But you need referees for all sorts of reasons.
   A: Yeah, but sure it's more important that decisions are correct.
   B: Hmm. I suppose you have a point.

B Listen and mark the main stresses in A's sentences.

C Listen and repeat A's sentences. Pay attention to stress and intonation.

LEARN TO
CLARIFY IDEAS

3 A Put the phrases in bold in the correct order.

1. **A:** Do you like this dress on me?
   B: I prefer the white one.
   A: **you / is / so / saying / what / 're** this one, which cost a fortune, looks terrible.
   _____
   B: No, I mean the white one makes you look slimmer.
   A: **other / so, / words / in**, I look fat!
   _____
   B: No, no, you're twisting my words. I just meant that you look *even* slimmer in the white one.

2. **A:** Don't you think we should pay a decorator to do it?
   B: **you / so / think / basically** I can't do it.
   _____
   A: I didn't mean that. It's just that it might be quicker and save us money.
   B: **what / you / so / mean / is** I might mess it up.
   _____
   A: No, but you're a perfectionist, and you know how long it takes you to do things.
   B: So, you'd rather spend money and end up with a worse job!
   A: Not exactly …

B Listen and check.

Do you like this dress on me?   Do you like me in this dress?

REVIEW 3: UNITS 5–6

GRAMMAR ARTICLES

1 Add *a*, *an* or *the* in ten places in the text.

If you want to win at sports, choose red shirt. Research by two scientists from University of Durham shows that team's chance of winning is influenced by color of their shirts. As part of their investigation, scientists examined soccer results since end of Second World War and found clear connection between wearing red and winning. Teams that wore orange or yellow shirt had worst records.

GRAMMAR REAL AND HYPOTHETICAL CONDITIONALS

2 Underline the correct alternatives.

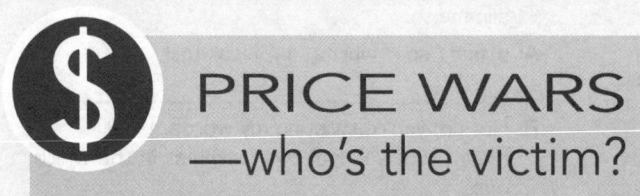

PRICE WARS —who's the victim?

If you ¹*own/owned* a store, and you ²*wanted/would want* to sell a product, you might put it on sale, but if you ³*would/were* to lower the price, you'd make less profit. However, if you keep the price the same but ⁴*would call/call* it a "sale price," customers ⁵*will/would* feel they're getting a bargain. Some other tricks are:

$ Ninety-nining—If the price ⁶*is/were* $19.99, it seems like 19-something. If the same product were priced at $20, it ⁷*doesn't/wouldn't* sell as well.

$ Buy one, get one free—If you ⁸*buy/bought* two items, the less expensive one is "free." In fact, ⁹*provided/supposing* the store is not losing money, you ¹⁰*can/could* be sure that the profit is included in the price of the more expensive item. ¹¹*Unless/Provided* you really need two items, you end up buying more than you planned.

$ Baiting—This is when an already cheap product is offered even cheaper. ¹²*Unless/If* you're not very disciplined, once you get into the store, you'll buy other things.

VOCABULARY PLUS COMPOUND NOUNS

3 A Join a word from box A with one from box B to complete sentences 1–7.

A

| out draw break down trade out break |

B

| through down off look back side come |

1 Its discovery made cooking possible and was a _____ in human evolution.
2 As more and more of us get our news online, the _____ for their survival is poor.
3 It can be hard to read, but the main _____ is that it's yet another gadget to carry around.
4 This is the best solution when there is a complete _____ in a marriage.
5 People stayed up to hear the _____ and to find out who would be the next president.
6 There are lots of positives, the only _____ is that you have to take it for a walk, even in the rain.
7 When people are choosing one, there's always a _____ between speed and safety.

B What is being talked about in sentences 1–7 above?

VOCABULARY ADVERTISING COLLOCATIONS

4 Complete the sentences with the correct word or phrase.

1 break into/promote
  a) There's a meeting in June to _____ trade between Scotland and Thailand.
  b) It's impossible to _____ the American market.

2 launch/advertise
  a) I hate it when they _____ something right after the opening titles of a program.
  b) The best product _____ uses a variety of media, like posters, TV and videos.

3 raised/reduced
  a) Because the products were faulty, it badly _____ our sales.
  b) When the movie star wore our clothes, it really _____ public awareness of our products.

4 enter/set
  a) Before you can _____ a price for your product, you have to know how much it costs to produce it.
  b) The power company GreenEnergi has taken over a competitor to _____ the market with lower prices.

REVIEW 3: UNITS 5–6   R3

5 gap /increase

a) Please don't _____ the price of rail travel—it's too expensive already.

b) They thought they had seen a(n) _____ in the market, but in fact there were lots of products online already.

6 dominated/endorse

a) Having a celebrity _____ a product is worth a month's advertising.

b) The collapse of the French bank _____ the news.

FUNCTION SUGGESTING IDEAS

5 Underline the correct alternatives.

A: Can we brainstorm ideas for Jack's going away present?

B: Could we go ¹for/toward a gadget of some kind?

C: What ²about/of something to do with cars?

D: I was thinking of something similar. For instance, it ³will/would be great to buy him a ticket to a Formula One race.

A: Would you ⁴consider/strike something completely different? Suppose we ⁵get/should get him a class?

B: What kind of class?

A: Well, how do flying lessons ⁶please/strike you?

B: I think we're on the wrong ⁷line/track here. How do you ⁸feel/think about a book on cars?

C: It doesn't ⁹strike/grab me. It's not original enough.

D: I agree. I'm ¹⁰torn/tearing between the Formula One ticket and the flying lessons.

A: Should we vote? OK, the Formula One ticket wins. So let's ¹¹go/do with that.

VOCABULARY OPTIMISM/PESSIMISM

6 Complete the underlined phrases.

A: So, how are you getting on with the course?

B: ¹I / mix / feeling / it. I'm finding the module on statistics very difficult. It feels like I'm ²nowhere / going, but I'm enjoying the other modules.

A: That's not surprising. Everyone ³have / their / up / down when they start college.

B: Yeah, but ⁴I / dread the exams.

A: Nobody ⁵look / forward / take / exams, but I'm sure you'll do fine. ⁶Look / bright / side. This time next month, they'll all be over.

1 I have mixed feelings about it
2 _____
3 _____
4 _____
5 _____
6 _____

GRAMMAR MODAL VERBS AND RELATED PHRASES

7 Complete the conversations with a modal verb or phrase.

A: Did you do the whole walk?

B: We ¹_____ climb to the top, but we ²_____ stay long because of the weather.

A: Were you ³_____ see much of the view?

A: You really ⁴_____ fly when you have the flu.

B: But if I don't get on that plane, I ⁵_____ to go to the wedding.

A: But when you try to check in, they might not ⁶_____ fly. The rules are pretty strict.

A: What time do your parents say you ⁷_____ go to bed?

B: I'm ⁸_____ be in bed by ten, but I often stay up till eleven. What about you?

A: I'm ⁹_____ stay up till ten on the weekend, but my parents ¹⁰_____ me go to bed at nine during the week.

FUNCTION PERSUADING

8 Complete the conversation with the words in the box. You do not need to use three words.

> shouldn't   surely   doesn't   wouldn't   haven't
> aren't   clearly   don't   isn't

A: Tom, ¹_____ you think we should start packing?

B: ²_____ it won't take all night to pack. We don't leave till noon.

A: ³_____ we at least begin? Last time it took ages—⁴_____ we didn't allow enough time then.

B: Only because I couldn't find my glasses!

A: Exactly. So ⁵_____ it better to do it now to give ourselves plenty of time?

B: You could start. I'll just throw in a few things later.

A: But ⁶_____ it be quicker if we did it together?

going away present   leaving present

REVIEW 3: UNITS 5-6

GRAMMAR FUTURE PERFECT AND CONTINUOUS

9 Complete the articles with the future perfect or continuous form of the verbs in the boxes. If neither is possible, use the future simple.

> not save   discuss   pay   face   double

By 2025

By 2025, in many countries, the number of people over sixty-five ¹_____, and far fewer people of working age ²_____ taxes to support them. It is almost certainly the case that many older people ³_____ enough for their old age and ⁴_____ an uncertain future or one of poverty. Experts from many different countries ⁵_____ the issue in Stockholm over the course of the next week.

> work   have   replace   not drive   live

By 2050

Sixty percent of humanity ⁶_____ in cities. They ⁷_____ gas or diesel cars. All cars ⁸_____ hybrid engines so that they run on electricity as well as a more traditional fuel. Robots ⁹_____ humans in all boring, mundane jobs, and, as a result, people ¹⁰_____ in more stimulating jobs but with fewer hours.

VOCABULARY PLUS WORD BUILDING: PREFIXES

10 A Find ten words with negative prefixes in the word square.

H	C	K	P	D	O	K	H	K	H	Y	F	N	U	S
X	J	A	Z	I	K	T	T	I	L	C	J	T	J	R
L	T	I	U	S	Y	U	N	V	U	A	U	V	V	V
G	H	N	N	S	Q	N	Q	X	N	T	E	G	I	Y
B	P	S	W	A	M	F	F	C	H	I	H	C	M	S
Z	I	E	I	T	E	A	A	Z	E	I	H	W	P	U
Y	R	C	L	I	D	M	L	X	A	L	G	M	A	P
I	R	U	L	S	L	I	Y	G	L	Q	Q	J	T	T
V	E	R	I	F	F	L	K	M	T	I	H	E	I	L
Y	L	E	N	I	A	I	P	O	H	N	V	E	E	S
L	E	H	G	E	Y	A	F	D	Y	V	D	V	N	U
B	V	X	I	D	S	R	I	Q	Z	X	R	C	T	B
E	A	U	U	N	R	E	A	L	I	S	T	I	C	K
M	N	M	I	S	B	E	H	A	V	E	N	T	Y	R
L	T	Y	M	I	S	I	N	T	E	R	P	R	E	T

B Complete the sentences with the words from Exercise 10A.

1 You eat three burgers and a pizza everyday? That's the most _____ diet I've ever heard of.
2 I'm sorry, but your point about aliens living on the moon is completely _____ to our discussion about science.
3 We asked for more money for the charity, but the government was _____ to help.
4 Many of our customers are very _____ with the new product.
5 Please don't _____ what Ahmet is trying to say.
6 Judy is really _____—you can tell by the way she bites her nails.
7 Wait a minute for me to find the right TV channel—you're so _____.
8 It's just _____ to think that we can score three goals in five minutes.
9 Cem's such a naughty boy—I can't believe how often I saw him _____.
10 Can you help me with the new software? I'm _____ with this program.

REVIEW 3: UNITS 5–6 R3

CHECK

Circle the correct option to complete the sentences.

1 I don't think he feels very safe, he seems very _____.
   a) unrealistic   b) irrelevant   c) insecure

2 Before the invention of _____, people paid for everything in cash.
   a) the credit card   b) a credit card   c) the credit cards

3 Great news! A Formula One driver has just _____ the company's new product.
   a) increased   b) reduced   c) endorsed

4 Caroline didn't want to go to college and went to work instead. Now she is _____ her first business.
   a) making   b) taking   c) running

5 There will be a bonus paid to all managers _____ they meet their targets.
   a) unless   b) provided   c) as long

6 Is it _____ to eat so much?
   a) unhealthy   b) insecure   c) unfamiliar

7 I think we're _____ nowhere here.
   a) coming   b) going   c) taking

8 The _____ for next year's harvests is very poor, and a widespread famine is predicted.
   a) outlook   b) outcome   c) downside

9 Children under thirteen _____ join social networking sites, but they often do.
   a) aren't supposed to   b) don't have to   c) aren't allowed

10 Are you allowed to _____ make-up at school?
   a) put   b) get   c) wear

11 Don't call me until the afternoon. _____ to our Washington office by then.
   a) I'll be speaking   b) I'll speak   c) I'll have spoken

12 She is very eager and imaginative and has _____ ideas for the future of the club.
   a) bizarre   b) predictable   c) brilliant

13 _____ your headphones today? I've broken mine.
   a) Will you be using   b) Will you use   c) Will you have used

14 A third runway has been approved at the airport. What _____ for local residents over the next few years?
   a) will that be meaning   b) will that mean   c) will that have meant

15 _____ buy the property, we would need to charge a high rent.
   a) If we will   b) Unless we   c) If we were to

16 _____ unfair that wealthy people pay a smaller proportion of taxes than those with less money?
   a) Don't you think   b) Isn't   c) Doesn't it seem

17 So _____ that no one knows the answer, they're just guessing?
   a) what you're saying is   b) what you're getting is   c) basically you

18 Contact lenses _____ eyecare in the mid-twentieth century.
   a) had a devastating effect   b) revolutionized   c) adjusted

19 The product has been _____ by leading medical experts.
   a) endorsed   b) raised   c) dominated

20 The whole feel of the website is very _____ and positive.
   a) upbeat   b) despairing   c) dreadful

21 The book is about a _____ sect or religion that existed in the fourteenth century.
   a) predictable   b) bizarre   c) unrealistic

22 At school they _____ three hours' homework a night.
   a) let us do   b) made us do   c) allowed us to do

23 There was a _____ in the talks at the very last minute, and an agreement has been reached.
   a) breakdown   b) breakthrough   c) trade-off

24 He won't play in the World Cup _____ completely fit.
   a) unless he's   b) if he's   c) until he'll be

25 He's amazing. He looks really _____.
   a) his prime   b) young for his age   c) immature

26 Would you consider _____ a consultant?
   a) hiring   b) hire   c) to hire

27 If I get high enough grades, I'll start _____ next September.
   a) the college   b) college   c) a college

28 The rise of drug abuse fills me with _____.
   a) upbeat   b) despair   c) mixed feeling

29 Last Tuesday, for the first time, scientists _____ communicate with a patient in a deep coma.
   a) could   b) were able   c) managed to

30 _____ is like jam—you can't spread even a little without getting some on yourself!
   a) The happiness   b) A happiness   c) Happiness

RESULTS /30

7.1

VOCABULARY
TELEVISION

1A Find sixteen words with types of TV programs.

D	O	C	U	M	E	N	T	A	R	Y	A	B	C
O	D	E	F	G	H	I	J	G	K	Q	U	I	Z
C	L	M	N	O	P	Q	R	A	S	T	V	W	X
U	Y	Z	P	A	B	W	C	M	D	E	F	M	G
D	E	T	E	C	T	I	V	E	H	I	J	I	K
R	L	M	R	N	O	L	P	Q	R	S	T	N	V
A	F	E	I	D	C	D	B	A	Z	Y	X	I	X
M	G	S	O	A	P	L	H	I	J	K	L	S	C
A	Q	E	D	P	S	I	T	C	O	M	O	E	K
S	T	R	U	V	W	F	X	Y	Z	A	B	R	R
I	H	I	G	S	K	E	T	C	H	F	E	I	W
J	N	E	W	S	K	L	M	N	O	P	Q	E	E
E	D	S	C	T	H	R	I	L	L	E	R	S	F
F	H	I	R	E	A	L	I	T	Y	K	J	M	T

B Complete the sentences with the words from Exercise 1A.

1 A _____ events program covers up-to-date social and political stories.
2 A _____ opera has romance and drama and is on regularly.
3 Number 8 down is one kind of _____ show.
4 A _____ program features animals.
5 A set of programs is a _____, for example, *Dancing with the Stars*.
6 A program about something real is called a _____.
7 A _____ mixes reality and fiction.
8 Actors wear clothes from the past in a _____ drama.
9 It's full of suspense. It's a _____.
10 A _____ show often puts ordinary people in extraordinary situations.
11 A private eye solves a murder every week in a _____ series.
12 Find out what happened today on the _____.
13 Competitors answer questions on a _____ show.
14 A _____ has the same characters each week in funny situations.
15 A short funny pieces are acted out on a _____ comedy show.
16 A _____ is a story or drama broadcast in different parts.

GRAMMAR
QUANTIFIERS

2 Cross out the incorrect alternative in each sentence.

1 He has *quite a few/many/little* English-speaking friends.
2 *Several/Every/Each* room has a whiteboard.
3 We have *a little/a small amount of/little* money left, so we can afford a coffee.
4 *Much/A small number of/A great deal of* time was spent explaining the error.
5 I'll buy *either of/all of/both of* them, I like them so much.
6 *A few/A little/Several* books are missing from the library.
7 I have *no/any/some* idea what to do if the car breaks down.
8 I can't see *any/many/no* reasons for sleeping here tonight.

3 Complete the report with the quantifiers in the box.

> several   another   a large number
> a few   no   quite a few   every
> plenty of   each   a good deal of

WHAT'S YOUR MEDIUM?

We asked you how you prefer to get information: via the Internet, TV, radio, or newspapers and magazines? Here are the results.

Internet: 67%

Unsurprisingly, ¹_____ people said that the Internet is their primary source of information, although ²_____ respondents said they never used it. Two main advantages of the Internet were mentioned by ³_____ people, indeed by most of them. One was easy access. ⁴_____ was up-to-date content. Both of these features were given as problems with newspapers and magazines.

TV: 21%

Surprisingly, ⁵_____ of respondents, more than 94%, say they spend more time watching TV than they used to, although about a quarter of TV viewing is done through the Internet. Both normal and Internet-based TV remain important sources of information and ⁶_____ of them has maintained healthy audience figures.

Radio: 7%

Just as Internet TV has been a boost to that medium, the Internet has helped radio maintain its status as a preferred source of information for at least ⁷_____ respondents who spend ⁸_____ time listening to their radios.

Newspapers and Magazines: 5%

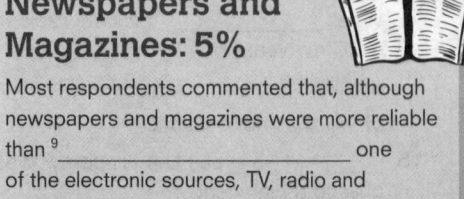

Most respondents commented that, although newspapers and magazines were more reliable than ⁹_____ one of the electronic sources, TV, radio and the Internet were all more convenient. Four people said that they use ¹⁰_____ other source apart from newspapers and magazines.

LISTENING

4 A Listen to four people talk about their favorite childhood TV program and complete the table.

Speaker	Program Name	Program Type
1		
2		
3		
4		

B Listen again. Which speaker (1–4) thinks:

a) Kids learned how to make things.
b) It was something kids understood better than their parents.
c) Every episode took kids on a journey.
d) If you made an effort you could win a prize.
e) Kids learned a lot that helped them with growing up.
f) Kids enjoyed the unconventional nature of it.
g) It involved a strong element of fantasy.
h) It was very realistic and right for the age group.

C Match the words in bold with meanings a)–f).

1 He's then transported to a world that **corresponds with** the outfit that he's wearing.
2 It's hard to underestimate its cultural **impact**.
3 It kind of **bridges the gap between** the two.
4 It deals with issues ... in an **unpatronizing**, **non-condescending** way.
5 One sketch would **morph** into another.
6 We'd spend our entire lunch break ... remembering all the **catchphrases**.

a) expressions which are linked to a performer or program and are very recognizable
b) appropriately intelligent
c) matches
d) connects
e) influence or effect
f) change

VOCABULARY *PLUS*
MULTI-WORD VERBS

5 A Complete the sentences with the words in the box.

> across   out (x 2)   up   back

1 If I say something offensive, I'm often too stubborn to take it _____.
2 If a homeless person knocked on my door in the middle of winter, I would put them _____ for the night.
3 Hard work brings _____ the best in me.
4 I come _____ as being more sociable than I really am.
5 If it turned _____ that my partner had lied to me, I would be disappointed in him.

B Listen to the sentences in Exercie 5A and underline the stressed part of the multi-word verb. Then listen and repeat.

C Complete the sentences with a multi-word verb from Exercise 5A but with a different or slightly different meaning.

1 I always buy a new version of a product as soon as it is _____ _____.
2 I can _____ _____ with a noisy hotel room more easily than a dirty one.
3 Smells rather than images _____ me _____ to my childhood.
4 If I _____ _____ a large amount of money in the street, I would hand it in to the police.
5 When a lot of people _____ _____ for a political demonstration, I'm usually not one of them.

D Check (✓) the sentences in Exercises 5A and C that are true for you.

7.2

READING

1 A Read the article about unauthorized use of pictures. Which of the following are mentioned as using photographs without permission?

- a professional photographer
- an electronics store
- a social networking website
- a telephone company
- a newspaper
- a city transportation company
- a travel agency

B Five sentences have been removed from the article. Complete the article using sentences a)–f). There is one sentence you do not need to use.

a) "The value of my work drops every time someone uses it without paying," he said. "I can't describe the anger I feel."

b) Who in the UK would ever find out that their image appears in a billboard ad somewhere in New Zealand?

c) "We think that amateur photographers should be happy for their work to gain so much exposure," said a company representative.

d) Or furniture. Or electronic appliances. Or cars …

e) "In fact, it didn't really bother us," he added. "But I can imagine someone else being very upset."

f) There are cases where the courts have not looked favorably upon the photographer's claim.

SAY "CHEESE" NOW … SUE LATER

The McGraw family of Dublin expected their visit to Poland to be full of adventure and surprises. But they never expected to find themselves ten feet high, beaming at the world from the wall of an subway station.

"We turned a corner onto the platform, and there we were in living color," said Paul McGraw. "It was a family picture that I'd posted on our family blog last year but in the middle of an advertisement for an electronics appliance chain. No one ever asked us for permission," added McGraw. "Someone obviously downloaded it from our blog." 1_____

The unauthorized use of photographs downloaded from Internet photo albums is not uncommon, and it would be impossible to count how many local advertising agencies have avoided costly photography and copyright fees by simply downloading material they find on the Internet.

"It's simply too tempting for them," said advertising lawyer Lee Szymanski. "In most cases, where the advertisement is going to appear in a small geographical area, the chances of getting caught are almost zero. 2_____ And if they do get caught, the legal process is too complicated, expensive, and frankly unclear for it to be worth pursuing."

As rarely as the culprits are caught, there are countless known cases of such "borrowing." In one case, a major cell phone provider used photographs taken from an Internet photo album site in one of its campaigns and justified it by saying that it was "promoting creative freedom." 3_____

Professional photographers have also been affected, and the law has not been clear in deciding if unauthorized use is legal or not. A California newspaper used a copyrighted picture taken by a professional photographer without seeking his permission, and, when he sued them, the jury decided it was a case of "fair use"—leaving the photographer with nothing but legal fees and frustration. On the other hand, a New York judge awarded a Quebec-based photographer over $60,000 in damages when he sued an online travel agency for their use of four pictures he had shot in Ghana. Meanwhile, the pictures had been duplicated and used on at least 200 other websites, according to the photographer. 4_____

"Professional photographers are in a better position to seek damages because they copyright their work," said Szymanski. "But for most people who simply upload snapshots to share with friends, there's very little they can do."

So the next time you upload a picture of yourself with a big grin, don't be surprised if you find yourself advertising toothpaste somewhere in the world. 5_____

unauthorized / subway   unauthorised / underground

GRAMMAR
REPORTED SPEECH

2 Underline the correct alternatives.

THE WORST INTERVIEW I EVER HAD – BY ACTOR RUDY SEARS

It was with a young journalist, and he started out by asking me normal questions. He asked how long it ¹*took/had taken* me to become successful as an actor, and I told him that I ²*didn't remember/hadn't remembered* a particular point where I could say I was successful. He asked who ³*did have/had had* the greatest influence on my acting style, and I said that my mother ⁴*has/had* —she was an amateur actress. Then he started on the personal questions: he asked if my marriage ⁵*was breaking down/broke down* and if it was true that my wife ⁶*wanted/wants* a divorce. I said I ⁷*won't/wouldn't* discuss that and that I ⁸*must/had to* go. In the end he wrote a very negative article about me, but it actually helped my career.

3 Change the sentences to reported speech.

1 **A:** Why did you come here today?
   He wanted to know _____.

2 **B:** I've been trying to see you since yesterday.
   I said that _____.

3 **A:** Please close the door and have a seat.
   He asked _____.

4 **B:** How can I help you?
   He inquired _____.

5 **A:** I have information that Mario the Snitch will be killed tomorrow.
   I told _____.

6 **B:** What makes you think this might happen?
   He wanted to know _____.

7 **A:** Don't waste time asking me questions.
   I told him _____.

8 **B:** Would you like me to let the cops know?
   He asked _____,
   and I told him it was up to him.

VOCABULARY
REPORTING VERBS

4 A Complete the interviewer's questions (1–6) and the answers a)–f) with the correct forms of the verbs.

Have you ever …

1 been persuaded _____ (take part) in a movie you didn't want to?
2 threatened _____ (walk out) of a movie?
3 suggested _____ (make) changes to a movie?
4 been accused _____ (lie)?
5 apologized _____ (do) something when you didn't mean it?
6 admitted _____ (do) something that you didn't do?

a) No, but sometimes I've refused _____ (say) "sorry."
b) Not usually, but once I told them _____ (change) my script in a key scene.
c) No, but I've done the opposite: denied _____ (do) something that I *did* do.
d) No, once I've agreed _____ (take on) a job, I would never leave halfway through.
e) No, not even when they've offered _____ (pay) me a fortune.
f) No, and in fact I always advise people _____ (be) honest.

B Match questions 1–6 with answers a)–f).

WRITING
A DISCURSIVE ESSAY; LEARN TO USE LINKERS OF CONTRAST

5 A Look at the sentences from an essay on the topic below. Are they for (✓) or against (✗) the topic?

Topic: Most information on the Internet is unreliable.

1 Most Internet writers are amateurs, but many give objective information.
2 The Internet is a convenient source of information, but its accessibility can also mean that this information, is not trustworthy.
3 Of course there's some inaccurate content, but it's the reader's responsibility to identify the reliable information.
4 Wiki contributors try to give accurate information but too many don't use reliable sources.
5 Many amateur news websites look serious, but that doesn't make them accurate.
6 These weaknesses exist, but there are reasons to trust much Internet content as well.

B Rewrite each sentence in Exercise 5A with the linker given. Pay attention to punctuation.

1 (although) _____
2 (while) _____
3 (however) _____
4 (despite) _____
5 (although) _____
6 (while) _____

7.3

VOCABULARY
THE PRESS

1 A Add vowels to make words.

1 s_ppl_m_nt
2 c_rc_l_t__n
3 s_ns_t__n_l_sm
4 _d_t__n
5 b___s_d
6 _d_t_r__l p_g_
7 f__t_r_
8 t_bl__d

B Complete the letter with the words in Exercise 1A.

To the Editor,

I am writing to complain about recent changes to your newspaper in the new ¹_____.

I believe I am typical of the paper's readers in that I am an ordinary working person and I strongly object to the ²_____ of some of your recent headlines and stories, which do not suit a serious newspaper like yours. This style of reporting and the new color ³_____ are more typical of ⁴_____ newspapers. Also, the recent ⁵_____ on the public transportation system was full of the reporter's own opinions and was very ⁶_____. I think you should save your opinions for the ⁷_____ since that's what it is for.

I am sure the reason for these changes was to increase ⁸_____, but it has made me decide to cancel my subscription.

FUNCTION
ADDING EMPHASIS

2 Rewrite the sentences using one of the emphasizing structures: *pronoun/noun + be + the one who* or *the + adjective + thing is*.

1 He's always watching the news channel, not me.
   He's the one who's always watching the news channel, not me.

2 You were asking about the celebrity news.
   _____

3 The story is incredible because all the people escaped safely.
   _____

4 The fact that people want to buy this paper is remarkable.
   _____

5 They want to have a big magazine launch party, not us.
   _____

6 The number of ads is ridiculous.
   _____

3 A Correct the mistakes in the underlined parts of the conversation.

A: ¹This is total outrageous. Your questions are very biased against the government. I've never heard such biased statements from a journalist before. ²Absolute incredibly.

B: Well, Secretary, ³you're the one who always telling the people that we're getting richer when the cost of living is increasing and our wages are staying the same. ⁴What on earth do you justify that?

A: Look, ⁵there isn't a way I'd say that if the data didn't agree! Having said that, ⁶I be think we can do better to help ordinary people and so we're going to cut gasoline tax.

B: ⁷That are a good idea, Secretary, but why are you introducing it now? Is it because the election is in two months?

A: ⁸That is so wrongly! Are you suggesting that we're making up policies to gain votes?

B: To be honest Mr. Secretary, ⁹the amazed thing is that you're denying making policies to win votes.

B Listen and circle the stressed words in the underlined parts of the conversation.

C Listen and repeat the phrases.

LEARN TO
MAKE GUESSES

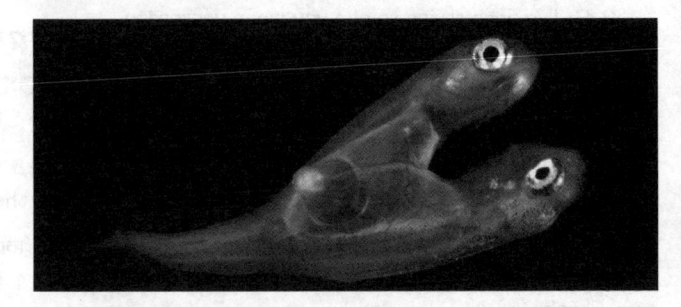

4 A Put the words in the correct order.

1 it's / reckon / I / fish / Siamese / a
   I reckon it's a Siamese fish.

2 it's / photo / hoax / a / surely
   _____

3 upstream / plant / perhaps / nuclear / a / there's
   _____

4 might / fish / be / it / two
   _____

5 imagine / it's / say / I'd / genuine / to / but / it's / hard
   _____

B Match sentence beginnings 1–5 in Exercise 4A with endings a)–e).

a) ____ —why would anyone fake it?
b) ____ just like twins who are connected.
c) ____ and this is a genetic mutation.
d) ____ with one on top of the other.
e) ____ and someone's just playing a joke.

Secretary   Minister

VOCABULARY
COLLOCATIONS: DECISIONS

1 Complete the sentences. The first letter of each word has been given.

1 Lying to him will g_____ a_____ all my principles.
2 I intend to s_____ t_____ my principles.
3 We're trying to a_____ the situation to see what went wrong.
4 They can't p_____ o_____ the decision any longer. We need an answer.
5 The committee has agreed to p_____ their decision until they have more facts.
6 Are you asking me to b_____ all my principles?
7 You should f_____ your principles rather than chase fame and fortune.
8 Sue's asked us to e_____ the situation and give a recommendation.
9 He'll need to e_____ the situation and get all the information about it.
10 When do you think the government will a_____ a_____ a decision?
11 We will have to l_____ i_____ the situation in detail.
12 At the end of this long discussion, we can finally r_____ a decision.

VOCABULARY PLUS
COMPOUND ADJECTIVES

2 Complete the newspaper headlines. Form compound adjectives with one word from box A and one from box B.

A

| time life long 15-meter third record five-year twenty-story |

B

| consuming time long high changing running high breaking |

1 Kidnappers given _____ jail sentences.
2 Woman survives fall from _____ building.
3 No solution to Russia and China's _____ argument over oil.
4 Jules Fane wins cycling race for _____ tenth time.
5 Voting too _____ for young people—survey reveals under-18s won't vote.
6 Prisoners escape over _____ wall.
7 Two million dollars for _____ lucky lottery winner.
8 Shirley Grey has _____ experience: singer leaves stage for charity work.

LISTENING

3 A You are going to listen to a lecture about an experiment to test people's behavior. Look at the posters. What do you think the experiment was about?

B Listen to Part 1 and check your ideas.

C Listen again. Complete the summary using no more than three words for each answer.

The lecture is about differences between people's behavior when they ¹_____ and how they behave when they ²_____.
It is in three parts:
1 A description of ³_____ at Newcastle University.
2 What this tells us about ⁴_____ and behavior.
3 A comparison with other key findings in the area.
The aim of the experiment was to discover whether the ⁵_____ that you are being watched can alter your behavior.
The scientists monitored ⁶_____ in a staff room to see how much people paid for their tea and coffee. Above it was a poster with the prices. Each week they ⁷_____ on the poster. They found that people were ⁸_____ when they were watched by eyes than when there were pictures of flowers. They put ⁹_____ as much money in.

D Listen to Part 2 and answer the questions.

1 Why is it important that our brains respond to faces and eyes?
2 How do people behave if they think they are being watched?
3 How did the researchers feel about the results?
4 How could a similar poster be used for speed cameras?
5 Where else could a poster be put?

8 behavior

8.1

8.1

GRAMMAR
PAST AND MIXED CONDITIONALS

4 A Read the articles and find the mistake in each picture.

DOLLAR-MILLION DILEMMA

One morning in 2014, Jim Farley was outside a Dublin bank when five bundles of cash fell from a security van that was driving away. He took them home and kept them for two days before calling the bank. He called from a pay phone in a terrible state of anxiety because he didn't know what to do. The security director persuaded him to hand in the money. It came to almost $1,000,000.

PARIS MÉTRO RESCUE

Jean LeBois was waiting for his métro train with his son, Roger, age four. Suddenly, a man collapsed on the platform and then fell onto the tracks. A train was approaching and LeBois had to make a split-second decision whether to help. He leapt off the platform and pressed the man into the space between the tracks. Five carriages went overhead before the train stopped. Both men emerged safe to the applause of the onlookers.

B Read the articles again and complete the sentences.

1 If Jim _____ (not walk) by the bank that day, he _____ (not see) the money.
2 His call _____ (trace) if he _____ (call) from a cell.
3 If he _____ (not come forward) with the money, it's possible that the police _____ (never find) it.
4 He _____ (keep) the money if he _____ (not speak) to the security director.
5 Jim _____ (be) rich now if he _____ (keep) the money.
6 The man _____ (not fall) off the platform if he _____ (not collapse).
7 If the train _____ (stop), Jean _____ (not leap) onto the tracks.
8 The man _____ (be) dead now if Jean _____ (not jump) onto the tracks.
9 If the space _____ (not be) really deep, both men _____ (kill) by the train.
10 If Jean _____ (have) more time to think, he probably _____ (not jump).

5 Complete the second sentence so that it has a similar meaning to the first. Use between two and five words including the word given.

1 I didn't know who he was, so I didn't ask him for an autograph.   HIM
If I'd known who he was, I _____ for an autograph.
2 You feel sick now because you ate too much.   SICK
You _____ if you had eaten less.
3 Anya's skis weren't very good, and this could be the reason she didn't win the race.   MIGHT
Anya _____ if she'd had better skis.
4 The ambulance took a long time. Is that why they couldn't save him?   COULD
If the ambulance had gotten here sooner, _____ saved?
5 You're living in a one-bedroom apartment today because you didn't take my advice.   LIVING
If you'd taken my advice, _____ in a one-bedroom apartment today.
6 You weren't paying attention, so you didn't hear what I said.   IF
You would have heard what I said _____ attention.
7 Angie left the GPS behind, and we're lost.   LOST
We wouldn't _____ remembered the GPS!
8 In my situation, what other choices were there?   YOU
What _____ if you'd been in my situation?

6 A Listen and write the phrases you hear.

1 _____
2 _____
3 _____

B Listen again and mark the stressed words and any examples of weak forms with /əv/. Then listen and repeat.

GPS   sat-nav

READING

1 A Look at the picture. Which position do you usually sleep in?

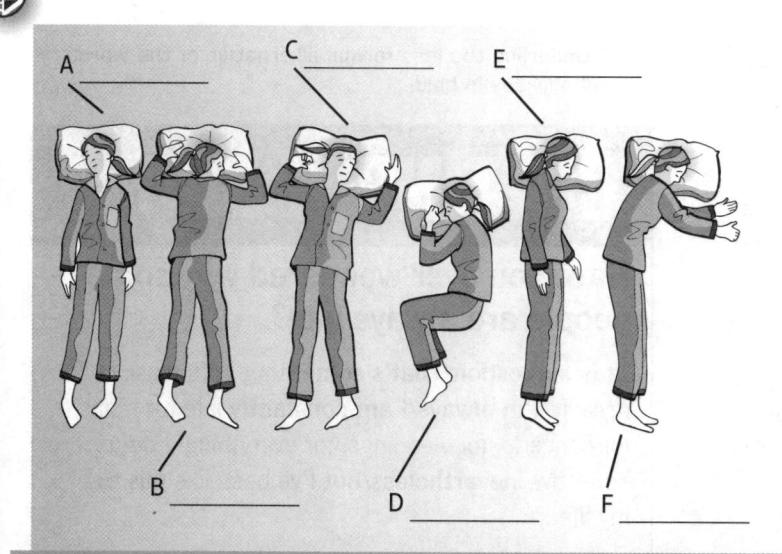

A _____ C _____ E _____
B _____ D _____ F _____

SLEEP POSITIONS GIVE CLUE TO THE NATION'S PERSONALITY

1 Some of Britain's best-known body language experts have been studying the four most common sleep positions for a well-known hotel chain. They think that our sleeping posture shows something about our character and how we see life. They believe that how we sleep reflects how we spent our day—under stress, relaxed and happy, bored and uncomfortable, feeling in or out of control. Here are the findings from the study.

2 Over half of people in Britain sleep with our knees up and our heads down. It's called the fetal position, and more women than men sleep like this. People sleeping in this position are seeking comfort from the stresses and worries of their day. They are often shy and sensitive to others and like their lives to be ordered and under control.

3 The next most common position is the Log. As the saying goes, people who "sleep like a log" lie on their side with their body straight and their arms down by their side. These people are trusting, easy-going and likely to be popular and part of the in-crowd. Unfortunately they often tend to be too trusting of other people, even to the point of being gullible. Around one third of British people adopt this sleep position. This position needs to be contrasted with the Soldier position in which people sleep on their back with their arms very close to them. It is said that people who sleep in this position are quiet perfectionists who have high expectations of themselves and others and really don't like to make a fuss about things.

4 A significant number of people in the UK sleep in the Yearner position with their arms out in front of them, as if they are chasing something. People who sleep in this position are open to possibilities but can be cynical. Worse still, once they make a decision—a good one or a bad one—they are not going to change their mind. Two similar positions are the Starfish and the Freefaller. People sleeping in the Starfish posture, lie on their back with both their hands above their heads. These people make great friends because they are good listeners and tend to be very supportive.

5 Freefallers make up the fourth major group of British people. Freefallers sleep lying on their front with their arms outstretched, as if they were falling through the sky. They feel that they are not in control of their lives, and, although they tend to be gregarious, below the surface they are nervous and thin-skinned.

6 So, with over 70% of British people sleeping in the fetus or Freefall positions, the picture indicates that the UK is a worried and anxious nation.

fetal / fetus   foetal / foetus

B Read the article and label the pictures of the sleeping positions with the names.

C Which type of person are the quotes 1–6 about? Underline the part of the article which helped you decide.

1 "Freida is always talking to people and gossiping, but, if you say anything bad about her, she really doesn't like it."
2 "Go and talk to Sarah, she always makes time to listen to people."
3 "We threw a surprise party for him, and he almost died of embarrassment."
4 "No, you can't persuade him. He's decided what he wants."
5 "Yeah, he wants everything to be perfect, so we're always working late."
6 "He loves a good party, and he's so laid back."

D Find words in the article which mean:

1 physical position (paragraph 1)
2 a small group of people seen by others to be particularly popular or fashionable (paragraph 3)
3 ready to believe anything (paragraph 3)
4 anxious or excited behavior often about unimportant things (paragraph 3)
5 someone who likes being with other people (paragraph 5)
6 too sensitive (paragraph 5)

VOCABULARY

VALUES

2 Rearrange the letters in bold to make words. The first letter is underlined.

1 Dave really lost o**c**lntor of the meeting when the staff members started to shout.
2 Our company is very proud of its strong policies on **u**lityeaq.
3 My football team really shouldn't have lost the game—there's no c**u**jstie sometimes.
4 Anyone with a sense of **r**snefais would say that Renata was the better player even though she lost.
5 PC games are really bad for young people—they fill them with g**r**esagsino.
6 Demet's **r**eegd made her spend all the prize money instead of sharing it with her family.
7 I find **o**siygtener one of the most appealing characteristics in a person.
8 You'll need to ask the boss—she's the one with all the **w**pore in this organization.

GRAMMAR
-ING FORM AND INFINITIVE

3 A Underline the correct alternatives.

Scientists are learning more and more about sleeping and waking states. For example, did you know that ¹*daydream/daydreaming* can help you ²*to solve/solving* complex tasks? This is because it activates the part of the brain associated with ³*tackle/tackling* difficult problems. Also ⁴*take/taking* a nap in the middle of the day refreshes your brain. It's like ⁵*to clear/clearing* your email inbox so that there's room for new information. Interestingly, ⁶*stay up/staying up* all night, as many students do before exams, increases the ability to hold new facts by forty percent. Some people don't seem ⁷*to need/need* much sleep. UK prime minister Margaret Thatcher was famous for ⁸*be able/being able* to run the country on just four hours sleep a night. However, the great scientist Albert Einstein tended ⁹*require/to require* ten hours a night, perhaps because he solved problems by ¹⁰*sleep/sleeping* on them.

B Which fact in the text above do you think is incorrect?

4 Write sentences. Use an *-ing* form, an infinitive or an infinitive + *to*.

1 When / I / be / young, my father / teach / me / work hard / play hard.
   When I was young, my father taught me to work hard and play hard.

2 Jake / hate / not / able / play / football / because of his bad leg.

3 They / have / invite / Guido / give / talk / at / the conference.

4 Olga / have / suggest / go for / picnic.

5 What / you / want / me / do?

6 Would / you / mind / tell / us / how old / you / be?

7 The firm / not / expect / have to / pay for / the damage.

8 Can / I / persuade / you / change / your mind?

9 It / not be / worth / wait / any longer.

WRITING
AN INFORMAL ARTICLE; LEARN TO USE LINKERS OF PURPOSE

5 A Underline the less formal alternative of the words and phrases in bold.

CUTTING IT SHORT

Have you ever wondered why some people are always late?

¹**It is a question/That's something** I often ask myself. ²**I'm always/I am constantly** late for trains, for concerts, for weddings, for everything! I do try, honestly, ³**nevertheless/but** I've been like this all my life.

People hate latecomers. If you arrive late at a meeting, ⁴**it is thought/people think** you're lazy or disorganized or you don't actually ⁵**think much of/respect** the other people there. But that isn't true. We time-challenged people live a life of constant anxiety and stress. I can't begin to count the money ⁶**that has been wasted/I've wasted** by missing planes, classes, hair appointments, not to mention the stress of continually apologizing for messing up other people's schedules.

However, help is at hand. If you're someone who always cutting it short, here are some suggestions to help you ⁷**get over/recover from** this chronic problem. First of all …

B Do you identify with the writer of the article?

C Correct the mistakes with linkers of purpose in the sentences.

1 Sara was late because of her alarm clock wasn't working properly.

2 You should make sure you put things in your calendar in order remind you to do them.

3 Yuan went to the movie theather early to getting a good seat.

4 Take your car keys so that as you can drive if you get tired of walking.

5 You need to study hard so to get good grades.

6 Because I was late, I waited until the break to go into class so as to upset the other students.

7 On order not to disturb the boss, don't talk outside that room—she's in an important meeting.

8 We use an online meeting maker so as get agreement from everyone on the best time to meet.

D Complete the article in Exercise 5A with three suggestions and a conclusion (150–200 words).

VOCABULARY
BEHAVIOR

1 A Add vowels to make words.

1 d_pl_m_t_c
2 c_nfr_nt_t__n_l
3 s_ns_bl_
4 s_pp_rt_v_
5 c_ll_b_r_t_v_
6 s_ns_t_v_
7 _nh_lpf_l
8 _ss_rt_v_
9 f_c_s_d
10 t_ctf_l
11 _ggr_ss_v_
12 d_r_ct

B Which adjectives above are positive (+), negative (-) or can be either (+/-)?

C Match the adjectives in Exercise 1A with quotes 1–10. Sometimes two adjectives are possible.

1 "You're late again, Jones! Get into my office and sit down! Now!" _____

2 "Oh, you look really tired. Lie down and rest. I'll bring you a cup of tea." _____

3 "I prefer you in the other dress. This one makes you look overweight." _____

4 "You touched the ball! You cheat!" _____

5 "I'll work on the charts for the report while you edit the text." _____

6 "Look, I'm not angry, but just tell me, why did Louise get a pay raise when I didn't?" _____

7 "OK, everyone. I think we're straying from the point. We need to get back to the main issue." _____

8 "We don't deal with problems with your connection. You need to phone your broadband provider. You've already tried them? Well, it has nothing to do with us." _____

9 "It's true that I don't have the receipt, but I only bought it here last week. Could I speak to your supervisor. She's at lunch? No problem, I'll wait." _____

10 "If you want to lose weight, don't go on an extreme diet. Just eat slightly less and try and walk for half an hour a day." _____

FUNCTION
HANDLING AN AWKWARD SITUATION

2 A Put the words in the correct order to complete B's part of the conversation.

A: Is everything OK?
B: ¹I've / to / talk / something / about / been / there's / to / you / Actually, / meaning / .
_____

A: Oh, is there a problem?
B: ²you / get / the / to / want / wrong / I / don't / idea, / but / …
_____

A: That sounds bad.
B: ³you / just / cell / leave / on / that / often / It's / your / .
_____

A: I don't understand.
B: ⁴you're / annoying / And / it / and / that's / not / rings / when / here / .
_____

A: But I need to keep it on in case my son phones.
B: ⁵disturbing / trying / but / Yes, / people / are / work / when / to / it's / .
_____

A: It's important that he can get straight through to me.
B: ⁶I'm / understand / from / see / but / you / where / I / do / coming / ?
_____

A: I suppose so.
B: ⁷set / it / silent / you / when / could / not / to / here / Maybe / you're / .
_____

A: What you mean just the "vibrate" setting?
B: ⁸feel / about / you / Yes, / how / would / that / ?
_____

A: OK, that sounds reasonable. I'll do that from now on. Sorry about that.
B: Thanks, I'd appreciate it.

B Listen to the conversation and repeat B's part. Pay attention to the stress and intonation.

LEARN TO
SOFTEN A MESSAGE

3 Listen to B's part of the conversation and add the extra words you hear to the conversation in Exercise 2A.

pay raise / pay rise

R4 REVIEW 4: UNITS 7–8

GRAMMAR QUANTIFIERS

1 A Read the descriptions and correct a quantifier in each sentence by crossing out, changing or adding one word.

1 Floor-to-ceiling windows allow you to enjoy lots of fantastic views of the city while the city enjoys plenty fantastic views of you.

2 The apartment is in need of a little redecoration and lighting, but it benefits from a large amount of walls, floors and ceilings.

3 A few apartments with such excellent views ever come on the market, and, because it is currently owned by an artist, each room is uniquely decorated.

4 The apartment would be suitable for either a mushroom grower or someone who loves caves, since quite a few the rooms are on the lower ground floor.

5 The apartment is in a lively area, close to a large number of stores and several of clubs, so it would benefit from some double-paned windows.

B Read the descriptions again. What is the problem with each apartment?

VOCABULARY REVIEW

2 A Look at the underlined sounds in each group. Circle the word with the different sound.

1 b<u>ia</u>sed, d<u>e</u>ny, prom<u>i</u>se
2 r<u>ea</u>lity, thr<u>ea</u>ten, sk<u>e</u>tch
3 s<u>e</u>rial, c<u>i</u>rculation, gen<u>e</u>rosity
4 pers<u>ua</u>de, t<u>a</u>bloid, sens<u>a</u>tionalism
5 f<u>o</u>cused, c<u>o</u>nfrontational, c<u>o</u>ntrol
6 sen<u>s</u>ible, aggre<u>ss</u>ive, asse<u>ss</u>

B Listen and check. Then listen and repeat.

3 Complete the sentences with the correct word or phrase.

1 series/miniseries
   a) I can't wait for the next episode of the _____ to find out what happens next.
   b) They're doing a _____ on eastern cuisine; last week's was about Thai cooking, and next week's is from Malaysia.

2 sitcom/sketch comedy show
   a) Al Shaw stars in this _____ about a high-flying executive who suddenly finds himself out of work.
   b) Dean Murray is back in the _____ playing his familiar roles as the farmer who can't stand animals, the one-armed dentist and the policeman who can only speak in rhyme.

3 equality/greed
   a) He was surprised at his own _____. There was enough to share but he had eaten all the cake.
   b) She was put in charge of _____ issues in the company after she complained that women were not being promoted.

4 power/fairness
   a) There's no _____ in the referee's decision to send another Italian player off the field.
   b) The problem with concentrating all the financial _____ in one position is that no one else can make decisions.

5 explored/reached
   a) They _____ the options and decided to sell the hotel.
   b) They evaluated the situation carefully before they _____ a decision.

6 sticking to/assessing
   a) He's _____ his principles and refusing to reveal the name of his informer.
   b) He's _____ the situation at the moment.

7 sensitive/sensible
   a) She's very _____ to other people's needs.
   b) It's _____ to keep a note of your passport number.

8 assertive/tactful
   a) You need to be _____ when dealing with him so as not to upset him.
   b) You should be more _____. Don't let her bully you.

while / field   whilst / pitch

56

REVIEW 4: UNITS 7–8 R4

VOCABULARY PLUS MULTI-WORD VERBS

4 Complete the sentences by adding *across*, *back*, *out* or *up* in the correct place.

1 I'll have to take everything I said about the movie. It was terrific!
2 I don't like her in person, but she comes well on TV.
3 They're bringing a new version of the game next March.
4 Some old friends in San Francisco put me for the night.
5 The concert turned to be disappointing.

GRAMMAR REPORTED SPEECH

5 Complete the reported speech sentences. Use between two and five words including the word given.

1 "I want to leave school," Emilio said to his father.
TOLD
Emilio _____
to leave school.

2 "Could you sing something for us?" the guys in the band asked me.
WANTED
The guys in the band _____
something for them.

3 "You didn't give me your phone number," Ben said.
HIM
Ben explained that I _____
phone number.

4 "Why don't you like computer games?" Jane asked Rick.
HE
Jane asked Rick _____
computer games.

5 "Were you working for Sarah at that time?" Harry asked.
WORKING
Harry asked me _____
for Sarah at that time.

6 "I won't be seeing Katya until tomorrow," she said.
KATYA
She said she _____
until the next day.

VOCABULARY REPORTING VERBS

6 A Match the reporting verbs to the sentences.

> agree admit apologize promise offer
> suggest deny threaten refuse accuse

1 No, I'm paying for the meal. I won't let you. *refuse*
2 I'm sorry if I have caused any embarrassment.
3 We'll reduce taxes if you vote for us.
4 Unless I get more money, I'm going to quit the show.
5 You did it, Leona! You stole my wallet!
6 We'll share the information with you.
7 Let's take a break for a few minutes.
8 OK, I stole $5,000 from the bank.
9 I've never had cosmetic surgery.
10 You want me to make a speech? OK, no problem.

B Write reported speech sentences using the reporting verbs for each of the sentences in Exercise 6A.

1 He *refused to let me pay for the meal*.
2 I _____.
3 We _____.
4 She _____.
5 He _____.
6 They _____.
7 She _____.
8 He _____.
9 He _____.
10 She _____.

FUNCTION ADDING EMPHASIS

7 Complete the email extract with different words to complete the phrases that add emphasis.

> The people in the apartment below us are driving us ¹_____ crazy. Last Friday, they had an all-night party. I wouldn't have minded, but the thing ²_____ that they didn't warn us in advance and there was no ³_____ we could sleep through it. Why ⁴_____ earth do people need to have music so loud? I ⁵_____ hate it when people are ⁶_____ thoughtless. I had ⁷_____ a sleepless night that I was in a bad mood all day and had a ⁸_____ awful argument with Jack. It ended up with him shouting, "Well, you're the ⁹_____ who wanted to move here in the first place!" and walking out. Then the woman downstairs complained to me about the shouting! That made me ¹⁰_____ furious!

REVIEW 4: UNITS 7–8

GRAMMAR PAST AND MIXED CONDITIONALS

8 Complete the phrases. Sometimes there is more than one possibility.

A: Looking back over your career so far, ¹you / do / things / differently if you could start again?

B: I'm very happy with my choices, so, even if I could, ²I / not / want / change / anything professionally. As far as my personal life is concerned, I do wish I'd waited before settling down. ³If / Angela and I / not / get married so young, then ⁴we / still / be / together.

A: And ⁵if / you / were / give / advice to me as an up-and-coming actor, ⁶what / you / say?

B: ⁷If / I / start / again now, ⁸I / still / think / I / choose to work in the theater to get as much basic experience as possible.

1 _____
2 _____
3 _____
4 _____
5 _____
6 _____
7 _____
8 _____

VOCABULARY PLUS COMPOUND ADJECTIVES

9 Rewrite the sentences with the compound adjectives in parentheses.

1 I'm sorry, but I'll have to get back to work—this project takes a lot of time. (time-consuming)

2 In a race that broke all records, Daniel Nduka wins the London marathon. (record-breaking)

3 The company tries to save money then suddenly comes up with the funds when they're really needed. (money-saving)

4 I had to close my eyes before going into the room—it was so bright in there. (brightly lit)

5 I had to wait for five months before I had an operation to repair my knee. (five-month)

GRAMMAR -ING FORM AND INFINITIVE

10 Complete the articles with the correct form of the verbs in the boxes.

| express do look recognize be |

Right or Left: 1

Researchers in the UK have discovered that dogs tend ¹_____ at the right side of human faces. The right side is known ²_____ better at ³_____ emotional states. Interestingly, dogs don't seem ⁴_____ this when they look at other animals. ⁵_____ human emotions is an important skill for a pet.

| give sit have process watch |

Right or Left: 2

In an experiment, 74% of movie theater goers would rather ⁶_____ to the right of the screen. The right side of the brain is important for ⁷_____ emotional information. By ⁸_____ the movie from the right, people are choosing ⁹_____ themselves the best viewing experience. Interestingly, when told the movie was poor, people didn't mind ¹⁰_____ a seat anywhere.

FUNCTION HANDLING AN AWKWARD SITUATION

11 Underline the correct alternatives. In one case both are possible.

A: Ingrid, there's something I've ¹meant/been meaning to talk to you about.

B: Sure, Cristina. What's up?

A: I ²don't want you/hope you don't take this ³a wrong/the wrong way, but you often look very tired.

B: What do you mean?

A: ⁴It's just that/It's that just I've noticed you yawning sometimes, and, well, a receptionist needs to look more welcoming to clients. ⁵Do you know/Do you see what I mean?

B: You're right. I have been having difficulties sleeping recently.

A: How ⁶would you feel/are you feeling about getting some advice? From your doctor?

B: Yes, that's probably a good idea. Sorry about this, Cristina.

REVIEW 4: UNITS 7–8   R4

CHECK

Circle the correct option to complete the sentences.

1 That's not very _____ —telling her she's put on weight!
   a) collaborative   b) unhelpful   c) tactful

2 There were _____ things I would have changed but not many.
   a) quite few   b) a few   c) very few

3 The doctor told _____ to bed.
   a) that I should go   b) me to go   c) me going

4 I asked them to clean up the mess but they _____ to do it.
   a) refused   b) threatened   c) apologized

5 Companies should have rules about _____ so that no one is discriminated against.
   a) power   b) control   c) equality

6 My grandfather asked me _____ recently.
   a) what had I been doing   b) what I'd been doing   c) if I'd been doing

7 It's _____, but it looks like some kind of animal.
   a) difficult to say   b) imagine   c) seems to say

8 It was _____ fantastic news that I couldn't believe it at first.
   a) such   b) so   c) such a

9 You need to _____ the situation.
   a) follow   b) go against   c) assess

10 If Tom hadn't acted so quickly, they _____ now.
   a) might have been killed   b) weren't alive   c) could be dead

11 I'm trying to go to the gym twice a week _____ get fitter.
   a) so   b) for   c) in order to

12 _____ do it slowly, or you could cut yourself.
   a) You should learn   b) You'd better   c) Practice

13 I like factual programs, so I don't watch _____.
   a) documentaries   b) current events programs   c) reality shows

14 There is _____ traffic on the road because of the weather.
   a) hardly   b) very little   c) a small number of

15 Thousands of people _____ to vote.
   a) turned out   b) brought out   c) pulled out

16 Margit said _____ the next day.
   a) she'll do it   b) she'd do it   c) she's doing it

17 You often _____ good websites while you're looking for something else.
   a) put up with   b) come across   c) break into

18 I _____ him to call Washington.
   a) suggested   b) offered   c) reminded

19 There's a difficult situation I've _____ to talk to Kurt about.
   a) what I mean   b) been meaning   c) taken the wrong way

20 Louise Becker's _____ is read by millions of people every day.
   a) sensationalism   b) editorial page   c) biased

21 You're _____ wanted to come!
   a) one who   b) the one who   c) the one

22 I don't want _____ get the wrong idea, but …
   a) that you   b) you to   c) you

23 The paper has been accused of being _____.
   a) biased   b) tabloid   c) sensationalism

24 How long do you think it will take for them to _____ a decision?
   a) come to   b) arrive   c) stick to

25 If you _____ the lottery ticket, we'd be rich now.
   a) don't lose   b) didn't lose   c) hadn't lost

26 I really lost _____ of my temper when I saw that man kick his dog.
   a) control   b) fairness   c) aggression

27 If you'd been in my situation, what _____?
   a) would you do   b) would you have done   c) did you do

28 Hurry up. We have to run _____ to get to the concert on time.
   a) for   b) in order   c) so

29 _____ ticket costs $20.
   a) Each   b) Few   c) All

30 It's OK to speak your mind, but why are you always so _____?
   a) focused   b) assertive   c) confrontational

RESULTS /30

9 trouble

9.1

LISTENING

1 A Look at the pictures. Can you think of a reason why you might NOT notice the animals?

B Listen to the first part of a radio program and answer the questions.

1 What is the best definition of "inattentional blindness"?
   a) Losing your eyesight because of someone's carelessness
   b) Failing to see things that are obvious because you are stressed
   c) Not seeing one thing because you are focused on something else

2 Were your ideas about the pictures right?

C Listen to the rest of the program and put the topics in the correct order. One topic is mentioned twice and one is not mentioned.

a) pilots
b) motorcycles
c) drivers
d) soccer players
e) store security guards

D Listen again to the whole program. Are the statements true (T), false (F) or is the information not given (NG)?

1 A quarter of the people who did the gorilla experiment didn't notice the gorilla.
2 If you're looking for someone with glasses, you might not notice someone with a parrot.
3 Drivers who are sending text messages might not notice a car stopping in front of them.
4 If you expect to see a particular word or name on a sign, you might not notice a synonym.
5 In a simulation, trained pilots were better at seeing unusual things on the runway than non-pilots.
6 A thief is more likely to fool a guard in a store by stealing openly.
7 It's safer to drive a car than to ride a motorcycle.
8 The expert gives the advice "Expect the unexpected."

GRAMMAR
-ING FORM AND INFINITIVE

2 A Underline the correct alternative.

1 a) After high school, I went on *finding/to find* work in order to earn money.
   b) After high school, I went on *studying/to study* and attended college because that was expected.

2 a) I remember *locking/to lock* my apartment when I left it today, but it's possible that I didn't do it.
   b) I remembered *locking/to lock* my apartment when I left it today, I'm 100 percent sure.

3 a) I'm trying *learning/to learn* English well enough to pass an advanced exam.
   b) I tried *speaking/to speak* English in case they understood it, but they didn't.

4 a) I'll never forget *meeting/to meet* my English teacher for the first time.
   b) I've forgotten *doing/to do* my homework many times.

5 a) I had to stop *thinking/to think* about all of these sentences before answering.
   b) I've had to stop *thinking/to think* about my other work so that I could concentrate on this exercise.

6 a) I like *studying/to study* English at least fifteen minutes a day even if I'm not in the mood.
   b) I like *traveling/to travel* more than anything else.

B Check (✓) the sentences above that are true for you.

soccer players   footballers

60

3 Complete the story with the correct form of the verbs in parentheses.

MY DAY AS A POLICE WITNESS

It was 2014, and I had witnessed a theft—in fact, I'd tried ¹_____ (catch) the thief, but, when I caught up with him, he pulled out a knife, so I stopped ²_____ (chase) him and walked away. I remember ³_____ (stand) there, thinking how silly the situation was, before I gave up. I like ⁴_____ (be) helpful even when it's unpleasant or dangerous, so I didn't mind. Before I walked away though, I remembered ⁵_____ (memorize) his face, in case the police asked me for a description; but I made a mistake, because I forgot ⁶_____ (pay) attention to his height. Well, the police did call me a few days later and said they'd caught the guy and needed me to identify him in a line-up. So I went in, and looked at the eight faces … they asked me which was the thief, but I just went on ⁷_____ (look) at the faces, because they ALL looked like the thief. I tried ⁸_____ (picture) him with my eyes closed, but it didn't work. In the end I picked someone—the biggest, tallest one—because that was my recollection, that the guy was big and threatening. The one I picked turned out to be a police officer himself (who later went on ⁹_____ (become) the chief of police), and the real thief was the shortest guy in the line-up. On my way out, I stopped ¹⁰_____ (say) goodbye to the head detective, and he just said "Don't call us, we'll call you."

VOCABULARY
CRIME

4 Find ten words for crimes in the wordsearch.

A	M	C	A	I	P	R	I	C	B	C	H	L	S
R	V	A	N	D	A	L	I	S	M	K	Q	V	H
S	R	K	I	D	N	A	P	P	I	N	G	A	O
O	L	T	I	S	N	V	M	U	C	M	Q	Q	P
N	P	X	X	A	Z	Y	Q	H	L	N	K	R	L
Y	S	R	K	V	H	W	C	K	O	J	J	P	I
S	T	A	L	K	I	N	G	X	K	V	T	S	F
Q	Z	Z	W	A	V	P	S	H	E	C	V	D	T
W	L	P	S	V	S	H	A	C	K	I	N	G	I
L	V	Y	Y	L	C	B	R	I	B	E	R	Y	N
I	D	E	N	T	I	T	Y	T	H	E	F	T	G
C	O	U	N	T	E	R	F	E	I	T	I	N	G
W	Q	J	L	F	Q	B	M	U	G	G	I	N	G
F	U	Q	E	Y	J	R	N	V	P	W	C	O	H

VOCABULARY *PLUS*

5 A Complete the news stories by adding the dependent prepositions *for*, *from*, *with* or *of* to the verbs in bold. The prepositions don't always follow the verbs immediately.

February 5th—An Edinburgh man was ¹**charged** murder today. Police say they ²**suspect** 48-year-old Bill Haller committing a series of murders, but a senior police officer says they will only ³**accuse** Haller one, the famous Scarsdale murder.

February 9th—A police car transporting prisoner Bill Haller crashed on the highway today and burst into flames. Haller managed to ⁴**rescue** the driver the burning vehicle just before it exploded. The mayor ⁵**thanked** the prisoner ⁶**saving** the driver (who by coincidence is the mayor's son) certain death.

February 11th—Bill Haller was ⁷**cleared** the Scarsdale murder today as police ⁸**arrested** another suspect the murder. The mayor praised the police for their detective work and ⁹**apologized** to Haller the mistake. Haller made a statement ¹⁰**criticizing** the police their actions and ¹¹**blamed** an ambitious senior police officer charging him without evidence.

B Read the stories again. Why do you think the man was released?

highway / motorway

READING

1 A Complete the article with the words in the box.

> pride   greed   sympathy   fear   curiosity

B The quotes are from people who fell for one of the scams in the article. Write the correct number of each scam next to the sentences.

a) That's strange, I can't access my email anymore.
b) I sent the subscription form in and the money last week. They haven't replied yet.
c) Everyone should give something, we can't just let them starve.
d) Look at this. I have an uncle in Italy. Or I used to have one.
e) Excuse me, I'm here for the awards. I believe there's a room booked in my name.

C Match the meanings 1–8 with the words and phrases in bold in the article.

1 takes advantage of
2 it really exists, and it's legal
3 unfortunate situation
4 fame
5 clever and indirect
6 you can't check it
7 weakness
8 fake

FIVE REASONS YOU'LL FALL FOR AN INTERNET SCAM

Most of us think we're too clever to be caught by an email scam, but hustlers know they can always find someone naive enough to fall for their tricks. They also know five key facts about human nature, and one of these is behind every email scam you'll come across.

1 _____: You would think people would learn, but the desire for more money is our greatest **vulnerability**. From the instant lottery ("You've already won!") to an inheritance from the relative you never knew you had, the scam always aims at the same thing: to get you to pay in advance in the hope that you'll get back ten or a hundred times that much later.

2 _____: It's amazing how many of us imagine we've written a great novel, or at least a good poem, and have such a strong desire for **recognition** that we'd actually pay for it. The publishing scam works in clever stages, starting with a simple request to submit your poem. You then find out it's been chosen as a semi-finalist in a poetry contest; you only need to send in some money to register. Eventually you're asked for a large amount of cash to cover travel costs so that you can go and receive your prize at the (non-existent) presentation ceremony!

3 _____: If you find yourself paying for a "premium subscription" to a service that promises to give you access to information—about yourself or someone else—you might be paying for a genuine, functioning service, but it might just be another scam that **preys on** your desire to know more. These often start out by telling you that THEY have information about YOU and that you can protect that information by subscribing; or they offer information about anyone you want. There <u>are</u> agencies that really do sell personal information (for example, credit ratings), but many of these offers are **bogus**.

4 _____: The email may contain a direct threat with an equally direct demand for money or it may be more **subtle** and tell you that your bank account has been attacked and you need to enter your personal details, including your PIN, to protect it; or that your email account will be canceled unless you verify your password. Of course, once the scammers have this information, they can get to your money or pretend they're you and use that disguise to get money.

5 _____: Who can ignore a photograph of a suffering child or the **plight** of disaster victims in need? Sadly, for every **legitimate** charity in operation there are probably dozens of fake charities using our natural kindness and compassion to get us to transfer money to a bank account somewhere, but the end result is that we're just making millionaires out of the scammers.

So, if you've received an email from an **unverifiable** source and you're feeling greed, pride, curiosity, fear or sympathy, you're probably being scammed.

VOCABULARY
SYNONYMS

2 A Read the forum entries. Which thing do you think is the worst?

> **WHAT'S THE WORST THING YOU DID WHEN YOU WERE A KID?**
>
> - We went door to door, and we would ¹**pose as** boy scouts raising money for a charity. We used to ²**fool** everyone, but it wasn't hard—we had the right uniforms.
> - I used to ³**swap** my neighbor's newspaper every day for the previous day's paper. He never noticed.
> - My friend and I took candy from the local store. One of us would ⁴**divert** the storekeeper's **attention**, while the other filled her bag.
> - I used to ask people for change, and, when they took it out of their pocket, I'd ⁵**snatch** it and run away.
> - I told people I'd been robbed and needed two dollars to get home. They used to ⁶**fall for it** every time, and I made at least ten dollars an hour.

B Put the letters in order to make synonyms. The first letter is underlined.

a) sa<u>d</u>ttric   _____
b) ce<u>d</u>ivee   _____
c) <u>n</u>edterp ot eb   _____
d) <u>b</u>rag   _____
e) <u>s</u>cwiths   _____
f) <u>b</u>e keant ni   _____

C Match the words and phrases in bold in Exercise 2A with the synonyms a)–f) in Exercise 2B.

GRAMMAR
PAST MODALS OF DEDUCTION

3 Underline the correct alternatives. Sometimes there is more than one possibility.

A: Oh, no! It ¹*can't have/might have/must have* gone!
B: What's up?
A: You ²*might have/must have/should have* left the car unlocked. The doors are open, no windows are broken, and my bag's gone!
B: I thought I'd locked it, but I ³*might have/can't have/shouldn't have* left it open. I clearly remember locking it.
A: Or the thief ⁴*could have/must have/should have* been good at picking locks.
B: No, I ⁵*can't have/might have/shouldn't have* left it unlocked. I'm certain I did lock it. They ⁶*could have/must have/might have* picked the lock somehow.
A: Well, whatever happened, they ⁷*must have/can't have/might have* gone far. We've only been gone for ten minutes. Call the police.

4 Complete the sentences with a past modal of deduction and a suitable verb.

1 They _____ home yet—they only left half an hour ago, and it's 60 miles away.
2 Ali and Fátima _____ each other in college; they're always talking about their time there.
3 You _____ your keys when you took out your wallet, or maybe you left them in the café.
4 This essay is too good to be Leila's own work; it _____ from the Internet.
5 I _____ my hand while I was peeling the potatoes or maybe later.
6 But you _____ him in town yesterday—he's been abroad all week.
7 You _____ all my chocolate. There's no one here except me and you, and I haven't had any of it!
8 I think we're on the wrong road. We _____ a turning somewhere.

5 Listen and complete the sentences with a past modal of deduction and a verb. Then listen and repeat.

1 It _____ you.
2 It _____ me.
3 You _____ her.
4 They _____ there.
5 We _____ them.

WRITING
A "HOW TO" LEAFLET; LEARN TO AVOID REPETITION

6 A Put the words in order to complete the tips for how to keep secure at an ATM.

1 nearby / you / make / characters / sure / check / suspicious / that / there / no / are / .
_____

2 your / your / entering / be / cover / fingers / careful / PIN / when / particularly / to / .
_____

3 count / to / try / quickly / money / the / .
_____

4 your / put / to / time / take / safely / away / card / .
_____

5 if / to / attention / around / tries / your / turn / someone / get / never / .
_____

6 be / nearby / always / people / of / aware / .
_____

B Write six tips for a leaflet: How to avoid being a victim of identity theft. Use a variety of ways to give the advice.

9.3

FUNCTION
REPORTING AN INCIDENT

1 A Find the mistakes in the underlined phrases and write the correct versions below.

A: I've just been robbed, on the subway, by a pickpocket.

B: What happened?

A: Well, this guy got on the train, and ¹he reminded me to that English football player ... ²wait, my mind's gone blink. Oh, yeah, David Beckham.

B: David Beckham? Didn't you wonder why he was traveling on the subway?

A: ³It never occupied me, no. Well, then everyone crowded round with their camera phones.

B: Typical!

A: I had to push my way past them, and, ⁴before I was realizing what was happening, my wallet was gone, right out of my bag.

B: Did you see or feel anyone take it?

A: ⁵No, in fact only it was a minute later that I realized they'd done it. ⁶It was all happened so fast, and I was in a hurry anyway.

B: So the David Beckham lookalike must have been a distraction.

A: Yeah, and he must have had someone working with him.

B: Well, the people with camera phones, maybe they ...

A: Do you think so? ⁷They seemed to like students, but ...

B: Oh, definitely, it was a pickpocket gang. That's how they work.

1 _____
2 _____
3 _____
4 _____
5 _____
6 _____
7 _____

B Listen and check. Then listen and say A's part at the same time as the recording.

VOCABULARY
INCIDENTS

2 Complete the account of a bad dream with one word in each blank.

I was cooking when I heard a loud crash outside. I went out to see what it was—a driver had tried to avoid knocking ¹_____ a penguin crossing the road and had run ²_____ a second penguin who was just behind the first one. I was trying to help when the driver pointed at my window, and I saw that the frying pan was on ³_____. I tried the door, but I realized I'd locked myself ⁴_____. So I picked up the first penguin and tried to use it to break ⁵_____ the door. Its wings suddenly grew huge, and it flew off, so then I tried to climb in through the bathroom window, but I got ⁶_____. The driver pulled me out, and for some reason I then decided to climb onto the roof, but I lost my balance and fell ⁷_____. I must have gotten knocked ⁸_____ because the next thing I remember was opening my eyes and seeing Brad Pitt standing there with an empty bottle saying, "Sorry, we've run out of water." Then I woke up!

LEARN TO
REPHRASE

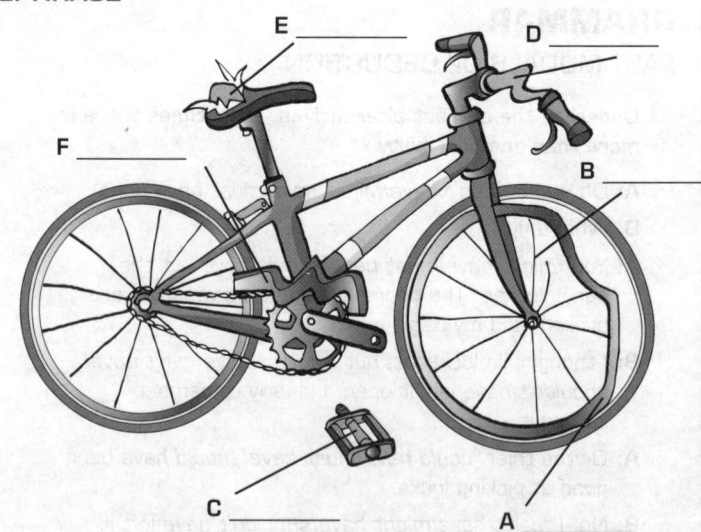

3 A Label the parts of the bicycle A–F with the words in the box.

| pedal   chain guard   handlebar   spokes   rim   seat |

B Listen to the conversation or read the audio script on page 81 to check.

camera phones   phonecams

READING

1 A Look at the picture and read the question on the forum. How would you answer it? Can you give an example?

B Read the forum and match comments 1–7 with categories a)–d).

a) sound   1
b) image
c) situation
d) other

C Seven sentences have been removed from the article. Complete the article with sentences a)–g).

a) I guess I identify with the character from the start, and so it feels like it's me who's trapped.

b) Maybe it reminds me of my early childhood, that feeling of being lost, of hearing my own voice crying out for help.

c) And then there's that fast part in *Friday the 13th*, they have the whole orchestra playing …

d) Darkness and shadow can have the same effect—the effect of hiding the evil character but letting you see just enough to imagine its shape and form.

e) You know that partly because they're not a main character and they're not needed to play the story out.

f) It's similar, I guess, when there's a sinister little boy or girl, or twins in old-fashioned clothes …

g) Some are also made from made-up compound nouns, like *Cloverfield*, *Skinwalkers*, *Wickerhouse*.

D Find words in the forum that mean:

1 make a high-pitched sound (paragraph 1)
_____

2 strange and frightening (paragraph 3)
_____

3 damaged or made immoral (paragraph 4)
_____

4 talking quickly (paragraph 6)
_____

5 quick moment (paragraph 7)
_____

MOVIE FAN FORUM

This week we asked:
What makes a horror movie scary for you?

1 I'm a big fan of horror movie music, and I think that's the thing that really carries the fear factor for me. You get slow creepy music like in *Jaws*, you know buh-dup-buh-dup-buh-dup-buh-dup, … ¹_____, or the screaming shock music like in *Psycho*, where suddenly when the shower curtain opens, the violins shriek incredibly loudly. Every time I see that scene, I jump out of my seat and it's the music that does it.

2 Vulnerability is what gets me. A character is put into a position where they can't really protect themselves against something terrible, whether they're alone, trapped in a closed space, or walking down a dark stairway or narrow hallway, or in a forest that's overgrown and hard to walk through, and basically not knowing what's going on, but knowing it's not good. ²_____

3 I think the title of a movie has quite an impact. If it's good, it somehow captures the whole experience of the movie, so even years after seeing *The Omen*, if I heard that title, I'd relive the feeling. The really good titles seem to follow a pattern, for example, "the" followed by a word ending with *-ing*, for example, *The Haunting*, *The Shining*, *The Vanishing*. ³_____ Or you get odd, eerie words after "the": *The Ring*, *The Uninvited* and, of course, *The Omen*. Very scary, I don't know why.

4 A kid's bicycle upside-down with one of its wheels turning. A broken doll. A child's shoe. I see a shot of one of those, and I hide under my seat. ⁴_____ I think it has to do with the innocence of childhood being corrupted by evil.

5 There's a kind of scene in a lot of horror movies that always gets me. I call it the "innocent victim" scene. You'll have a character who's often a very likeable old guy or old lady who does a simple job like running a store or working in a restaurant. What happens is something like they close up the store, get into their car, drive home in darkness, pull into their driveway … and so on, and you know that at any moment something very bad is going to happen to them, but you don't know exactly when. ⁵_____

6 When the sound track has sound effects that sound a bit like human voices, that really scares me. So like religious chants or women's voices chattering. You almost hear words but not quite. Or a child's voice, that gives me the shivers. ⁶_____

7 When you get just a glimpse of the villain or evil being. So he or she walks by a window or is spotted by a character just for a flash, and then is out of sight. ⁷_____ It really makes the evil come alive in your mind because your imagination starts racing, generating images.

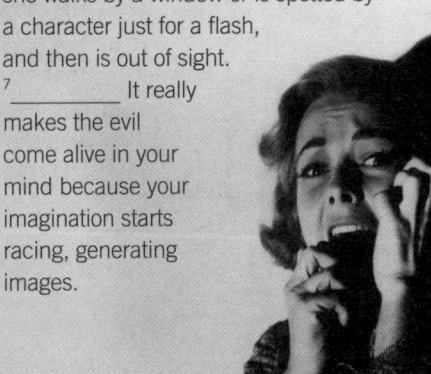

part   bit

10.1

VOCABULARY
ADJECTIVES TO DESCRIBE MOVIES

2 Add vowels to make words.

1 f_st-p_c_d
2 g_ry
3 hyst_r_c_l
4 c_ntr_v_rs__l
5 f_ll _f s_sp_ns_
6 gr_pp_ng
7 t__ _ch_ng
8 cr__ _py
9 __tst_nd_ng
10 th__ _ght-pr_v_k_ng

GRAMMAR
RELATIVE CLAUSES

3 A Underline the correct alternatives.

THE PROBLEM WITH MOVIE THEATERS

¹What/When/Whose I was younger, one thing I used to do was to go and see new movies as soon as they came out, but I've stopped because of the way ²who/what/that people behave there. The movie theater should be a place ³which/where/when you are transported to another world, but this is impossible because:

- a cell phone rings, ⁴when/which/what completely kills the moment. People ⁵who/whose/what leave their cell phones on are thoughtless; people ⁶who/whose/when phones ring should be sent out.

- people act like they're at home, by ⁷whom/where/which I mean they have conversations, sometimes ⁸where/when/which there's something really moving happening on screen. You hear about times in the day ⁹what/when/which something went wrong instead of the dialogue.

- children, ¹⁰which/who's/whose parents should control them better, kick your seat every time they laugh.

B In which examples above is it possible to leave out the relative pronoun?

4 Make sentences containing relative clauses with the prompts. The word in bold immediately follows the relative pronoun.

1 A biopic / be / a movie / **tells** / the life story / famous person.
   A biopic is a movie that tells the life story of a famous person.

2 The biopic / I want to review today / be / *Raging Bull*, / **be** / the story of a famous boxer.
   _____

3 Robert de Niro, / **play** / the part of Jake La Motta, / be / absolutely extraordinary.
   _____

4 The movie / be / made at a time / **most** biopics / be of heroic figures.
   _____

5 The movie, / **be** / directed by Martin Scorsese, / be / now recognized as a masterpiece.
   _____

6 De Niro / become / interested when he read the book / on / **story** / be / based.
   _____

WRITING
A REVIEW; LEARN TO USE ADVERB + PAST PARTICIPLE COMBINATIONS

5 A Rearrange the letters to make adverbs that collocate with the past participles.

1 ghlhyi _____ / ylediw _____ praised
2 hyhlars _____ / oyghlwelrminve _____ / eahvliy _____ criticised
3 klulfysil _____ / iisetvsynle _____ directed
4 ptlnnoagyi _____ / nlngvnoiicyc _____ acted

B Complete the sentences with one of the collocations above.

1 a) Audiences all over the world have applauded the movie.
   The movie has been _____.
   b) Critics have given it very positive reviews.
   It has been _____.

2 a) There wasn't a critic who said a positive thing about his last movie.
   His last movie was _____.
   b) The reviews weren't just negative, they were very negative.
   The movie was _____.

3 a) It wasn't an easy script, but Spielberg showed his talent in the way he directed it.
   The script was _____.
   b) The topic is a delicate one, but Bigelow showed she could handle this in her direction of the movies.
   The movie was _____.

4 a) The acting in that scene made me cry.
   That scene was _____.
   b) Morgan Freeman's acting was so good, I actually believed he was the real Nelson Mandela.
   The role of Nelson Mandela was _____.

GRAMMAR
PARTICIPLE CLAUSES

1 A Read the article and circle one mistake in each picture.

DAMAGED GOODS

When a woman ¹took/taking an art class at a New York museum tripped and fell into a Picasso painting, ²tear/tearing a six-inch hole in the canvas, the public gasped and giggled, ³shocked/shocking at how anyone could get so close to a valuable work of art. But museums, ⁴pressed/pressing to attract as many paying customers as possible, often give visitors considerable access to works of art, and this can carry risks. Similar incidents have happened in other collections.

- A visitor ⁵walked/walking down the stairs in a Cambridge museum stumbled into some 17th-century Chinese vases, ⁶shattered/shattering the vases into hundreds of pieces.

- A drawing by a famous artist, ⁷valued/valuing at over $80,000, was put through a paper shredder by a worker at a London auction house. The worker, deeply ⁸embarrassed/embarrassing by the incident, has managed to keep his (or her) identity a secret.

- A housekeeper ⁹employed/employing by a wealthy German family ¹⁰lived/living in a villa near Berlin knocked down a Ming dynasty plate.

- A painting by the Italian, Giorgio de Chirico, ¹¹displayed/displaying in a house in the Netherlands, was damaged when a demolition ball came through the wall, ¹²put/putting a large hole through the painting.

- At the London National Gallery, a painting ¹³was/being removed from a wall was broken in two. Apparently the glue ¹⁴used/using to hold sections of the frame wasn't strong enough.

B Underline the correct alternatives in the article in Exercise 1A.

2 A Replace the underlined phrases with phrases with participles. Make changes to the rest of the sentence where necessary.

1 The people who lived on the other side of the river were trapped.
   The people living on the other side of the river were trapped.

2 Anyone who is planning to go home early or who wants to take a break should let us know.

3 As I walked out of the restaurant, I ran into my old boss, who was coming in.

4 I used to work with the woman who lives next door.

5 I left the party quickly and didn't tell anyone that I was unwell.

6 She carried a child under each arm and ran out of the blazing building.

7 He jumped up because he was frightened by the loud bang, as he mistook the door for a gun.

8 Walls that have been painted white tend to attract more graffiti.

B Listen and check. Then listen and say the sentences at the same time as the recording, paying attention to stress and intonation.

VOCABULARY
THE ARTS

3 Add vowels to make words.

1 We couldn't get tickets, the show was a s__ll-__ __t.
2 He's what they call an "__lt__rn__t__v__" comedian, which means I wouldn't take my grandmother to see him!
3 The movie has gotten r__v__ r__v__ __ws in most papers.
4 It was a gr__ __nd-br__ __k__ng performance, completely different from anything I've seen before.
5 The show is amazing! A real m__st-s__ __!
6 Her interpretation of the role of Juliet has cr__ __t__d __ st__r among the critics.
7 They stopped playing small clubs once they went m__ __nstr__ __m and became popular.
8 The musical was a fl__p and closed after one week.
9 I don't know what all the hyp__ was about. She was awful!
10 The main dancer was sick, and someone else took his place, which was a real l__td__wn.

six-inch   fifteen-centimetre

10.2

LISTENING

4 A Look at the pictures. Which one do you think is better and why? Think of three reasons.

B Listen to Part 1 of a talk about how to take a good picture and circle the best alternative.

1 The main problem with the light is that …
   a) it's behind the photographer.
   b) it's shining into the lens.
   c) it's too direct and creates a flat effect.

2 The fact that the subject is in the center …
   a) is good because it's in sharp focus.
   b) is bad because it leaves space at either side of her.
   c) is bad because it cuts off her legs.

3 The problem with the background is that …
   a) it's not interesting.
   b) it's not completely in focus.
   c) it's a missed opportunity.

4 The person taking the picture …
   a) zoomed in too close.
   b) is standing too far away.
   c) didn't look at the woman's face carefully.

5 The last problem the speaker mentions …
   a) is that the woman is looking at the camera.
   b) is that the photographer is too tall.
   c) doesn't apply to this photograph.

C Listen to Part 2 and complete the notes. Use no more than three words for each blank.

THE FIVE RULES

1 Position yourself so that the light is coming _____.

2 Divide the screen into _____, and place the subject at one of the _____.

3 Make sure the background is _____.

4 You should be _____ to the subject.

5 Adjust your _____ so that the lens and the subject's eyes are at _____.

VOCABULARY PLUS
TWO-PART PHRASES

5 A Complete the advice for studying English.

Do you ever get sick and ¹_____ of feeling you're not making progress?

Everybody who learns a language has their ups and ²_____ along the way. Follow our dos and ³_____ for language study, and we guarantee your English will improve by leaps and ⁴_____!

DO find a place with peace and ⁵_____ to do your studying.

DON'T study off and ⁶_____, skipping days, or you'll make much slower progress. Spend at least ten minutes a day doing something in English, even just studying words.

DO watch a movie in English now and ⁷_____, at least once a month, and don't worry about understanding every word—just enjoy it!

DO record yourself in English once in a while and listen to the recording. Most cell phones can make a rough and ⁸_____ recording that's good enough for this task.

DO speak English with anyone who will speak English with you, even if their English is not as good as yours. There are pros and ⁹_____ to practicing with someone below your level, but in fact it can be very valuable because you'll be thinking in English.

DON'T cram! When you have an exam, look at the test date and plan your revision. Make sure you've completed what you need to do within your plan, give or ¹⁰_____ a few days.

DO learn from your mistakes. When you do a test or exam, go back and study the exam through and ¹¹_____ and think about how to improve weak areas.

There's lots more advice, we could go on and ¹²_____, but you should really get back to studying!

B Check (✓) which advice you think is good.

FUNCTION
GIVING A TOUR

1 A Put the words in the correct order.

1 visit / worth / it's / a / well
_____

2 the / over / let's / to / head
_____

3 to / they / interrupt / had / supposedly,
_____

4 not, / or / it / believe / took / it
_____

5 was / as / originally / it / built
_____

6 were / well, / founded / they / in
_____

7 he / that / goes / story / the / used
_____

B Listen and draw any links between the words in the phrases. Then listen and repeat.

It's well worth a visit

C Complete the conversation with phrases from Exercise 1A. Write the number of the phrase in the correct place.

A: Here we are at the famous Leaning Tower of Pisa. (a)_____ a bell-tower for the cathedral.

B: It looks like it's going to fall over!

A: It won't. Not today. (b)_____ 177 years to build.

B: Why did it take so long?

A: (c)_____ its construction because Pisa was constantly at war.

B: Didn't Galileo live in Pisa?

A: Yes. (d)_____ the leaning tower to demonstrate the rules of gravity, by dropping things off the top.

B: Is that true?

A: Who knows, really. (e)_____ Piazza dei Cavalieri.

B: Oh, yes, that's such a beautiful square.

A: Well, my favorite restaurant, Ristorante alle Bandierine, is on the way. (f)_____.

B: Sounds good to me.

VOCABULARY
DIMENSIONS

2 A Write the noun and verb forms of each adjective.

1 long — *length* — *lengthen*
2 short — _____ — _____
3 narrow — _____ — _____
4 wide — _____ — _____
5 broad — _____ — _____
6 thick — _____ — _____
7 deep — _____ — _____
8 high — _____ — _____
9 large — _____ — _____

B Complete the sentences with the correct form of words from Exercise 2A.

1 The jury needs to _____ down its choices before choosing the finalists.

2 He doesn't have much experience in other companies. He's a good candidate, but I think he needs to _____ his work experience.

3 The mystery of strange lights appearing in the sky in Russia _____ today as scientists said they couldn't explain them.

4 The _____ of the mixture is important—it shouldn't be too thin, so when you mix together the flour and water, wait for it to _____ before pouring it into the pan.

5 The _____ of the road isn't enough to add another lane—they'll have to _____ it.

6 We need to check the _____ of the sofa to make sure it's not too long.

7 Lessons should be shorter, and they should _____ the breaks in between.

8 This video tutorial will show you how to _____ a small picture.

9 The bridge was _____ enough for normal trucks to go underneath, but the _____ of those particular semitrucks was above the legal limit.

10 This exercise is too long—it needs to be _____.

LEARN TO
EXPRESS ESTIMATES

3 Correct the mistakes in the sentences.

1 There were under just 200 people at the party.

2 The homework should take you rough an hour to do.

3 We'll be arriving at 4 o'clock or so what?

4 The renovations cost downwards of one million dollars.

5 We're expecting somewhere on a region of a thousand people for the conference.

semitrucks / lorries

REVIEW 4: UNITS 9–10

GRAMMAR -ING FORM AND INFINITIVE

1 Underline the correct alternatives.

The Rules of Dinner Party Etiquette for Women (1950)

Dining in high society can be stressful if you don't know the rules. Study these, and you'll survive any dinner party.

1 When you are about to sit down, stop *letting/to let* the man next to you hold the chair for you.
2 Once seated, remember *turning/to turn* to your right and start a conversation with the man next to you.
3 If the man has forgotten *turning/to turn* to his left, gracefully join the conversation on your left and always try *looking/to look* interested even if you are not.
4 If another guest tells you they remember *meeting/to meet* you before, agree with them even you don't remember them.
5 If someone drops a dish, don't stop *talking/to talk*, just go on *having/to have* the conversation you were having.
6 If the person you're talking to doesn't seem to be listening, try *asking/to ask* questions—people love talking about themselves!

VOCABULARY PLUS DEPENDENT PREPOSITIONS

2 Complete the second sentence so that it has a similar meaning to the first. Use between two and five words including the word given.

1 He said he was sorry because he hadn't listened to her. APOLOGIZED
   He _____ to her.
2 People think that the website encourages bad behavior. BLAME
   People _____ bad behavior.
3 TV companies will no longer be allowed to show ads for fattening foods before 9 p.m. BANNED
   TV companies will _____ ads for fattening foods before 9 p.m.
4 Because of his quick reactions the plane didn't crash. SAVED
   His quick reactions _____.
5 Kelly had always wanted to be an astronaut. DREAMED
   Kelly had always _____ an astronaut.
6 The police think Jim helped the robbers escape. SUSPECTED
   Jim _____ the robbers escape.
7 She thinks I don't help enough. CRITICIZING
   She's always _____ enough.

VOCABULARY REVIEW

3 Complete the sentences with the correct word or phrase.

1 deceive/fall for
   a) I always _____ his compliments, even though I know he just wants a favor.
   b) It's not difficult to _____ people because most of us want to believe that everyone's intentions are good.
2 taken in/distracted
   a) They were _____ by us pretending to have a fight.
   b) Everyone was _____ by the trick, and no one saw the guy robbing the cash register.
3 ground-breaking/sell-out
   a) It was a _____ performance and changed the way people saw the character of Hamlet forever.
   b) It was a _____ performance and impossible to get tickets for.
4 letdown/flop
   a) After the success of their first album, the mild response to their second one was a _____.
   b) They were booked for five shows, but the first was a total _____ so the rest were canceled.
5 bribery/shoplifting
   a) _____ is common in the country, which is why if you have money you can get anything done.
   b) _____ costs supermarkets and other stores a lot of money. For this reason stores have increased security and made it more difficult for people to take things.
6 hacking/vandalism
   a) People in public life have to be careful of journalists _____ into their email accounts and publishing private messages.
   b) Examples of _____ are spraying graffiti on walls and breaking store windows.
7 narrow/shorten
   a) We'll need to _____ the time it takes to get the produce from the farm to the supermarket.
   b) Either I've put on weight or this door is very _____—I had to squeeze through it.
8 gory/gripping
   a) I find the plot of all of his books so _____ that I can't put them down once I start reading.
   b) I never expected a movie about animals to be so _____—I felt pretty sick at the sight of so much blood.
9 knocked out/knocked over
   a) He got _____ when his head hit the ice; he had to be taken to hospital.
   b) He got _____ during the football game, but he picked himself up right away and carried on.

football game | football match

REVIEW 4: UNITS 9–10

4
A Look at the underlined sounds in each group. Circle the word with the different sound.

1 res<u>cue</u>, t<u>ou</u>ching, m<u>u</u>gging
2 h<u>y</u>pe, h<u>ei</u>ght, g<u>o</u>ry
3 th<u>ou</u>ght-provoking, n<u>ow</u> and then, gr<u>ou</u>nd-breaking
4 rave rev<u>ie</u>ws, acc<u>u</u>se, f<u>u</u>ll of suspense
5 h<u>a</u>cking, c<u>au</u>se, f<u>a</u>ll for
6 hyst<u>e</u>rical, brib<u>e</u>ry, d<u>e</u>ceive

B Listen and check. Listen again and repeat.

GRAMMAR PAST MODALS OF DEDUCTION

5 A Read the two puzzles. What do you think the answers are? Write two ideas for each.

> **PUZZLE 1** A fully booked 747 took off from Hong Kong, bound for London Heathrow. When it arrived in London, there were no passengers on board.
>
> **PUZZLE 2** There were two men who were born on the same day in the same hospital. They had the same mother and the same last name. They looked exactly alike, but they weren't twins.

B Complete the conversation about the puzzles with *must/might/could/can't/couldn't have* and the correct form of the verbs in parentheses.

A: OK, so what about the plane puzzle?
B: The people ¹_____ (get) on the plane.
A: They did get on.
B: Then I'm not sure, but the plane ²_____ (experience) a problem and everyone had to get off.
A: No, there was no problem with the plane. I'll give you a hint: it wasn't a non-stop flight.
B: Got it! The plane ³_____ (make) a stop on the way, and all the passengers got off there.
A: That's right. So what about the second puzzle?
B: That can't be right, the woman ⁴_____ (give) birth to twins!
A: No, as it says, they weren't twins.
B: Oh. Then they ⁵_____ (have) the same birthday, it's impossible. Something's not right.
A: No: same birthday, same mother, same name.
B: I suppose there ⁶_____ (be) two mothers who were sisters …
A: No. Same mother. One mother.
B: This is only a possibility—they ⁷_____ (be born) a year apart, so they had the same birthday, but were one year apart.
A: No, it was the same year. Just minutes apart. But … they had a sister.
B: Oh! So they ⁸_____ (be) triplets!

FUNCTION REPORTING AN INCIDENT

6 Underline the correct alternatives.

A: So you let her in your door because she wanted a glass of water?
B: It just didn't ¹*cross/occur/seem* my mind that she was lying.
A: What, a complete stranger coming into your house?
B: She ²*occurred/seemed/reminded* like a nice person.
A: Didn't you see her pick up your cell?
B: Well it all happened ³*such/with/so* fast, but maybe yes.
A: So you saw it but didn't pay attention?
B: Yes. It was only ⁴*time/much/immediately* later that I realized what had happened.
A: How old was she, would you say?
B: She looked ⁵*as/about/like* she was about forty years old.
A: Can you describe her appearance?
B: She ⁶*reminded/remembered/looked* me of that actress …
A: Which one?
B: I don't recall, my mind's gone ⁷*blink/blind/blank*.
A: Did she introduce herself?
B: I didn't ⁸*cross/grab/catch* her name. It was probably false anyway.

GRAMMAR RELATIVE CLAUSES

7 Complete the article with *who*, *which*, *whom*, *whose* or *when*.

Chinese superstar Lang Lang, ¹_____ has inspired millions of young pianists and ²_____ performance was a highlight of the opening ceremony of the Beijing Olympics, was born in Shenyang in 1982. From the age of two, ³_____ his parents paid half a year's salary to buy him a piano, he was brought up to become the world's number one pianist. Lang Lang, ⁴_____ was naturally talented, won his first competition at five ⁵_____ he had to stand up to play the piano because his feet couldn't reach the pedals. His father, ⁶_____ gave up his job as a police officer, moved with him to Beijing for further studies, during ⁷_____ time father and son lived in poverty.

Nowadays, he is a young man for ⁸_____ playing the piano and being a superstar both come naturally. Lang Lang, ⁹_____ work as a Unicef ambassador is dear to his heart, has recently launched a piano competition for children, ¹⁰_____ is sure to be a great success.

REVIEW 4: UNITS 9–10

GRAMMAR PARTICIPLE CLAUSES

8 Complete the articles with the present or past participle of the verbs in the boxes.

> spend   use   live   find   kill

NUMBERS: People

5.5 liters: the amount of blood ^{1}_____ in the human body

13: the percentage of the world's population ^{2}_____ in deserts

25: the number of years ^{3}_____ asleep if you live to seventy-five

70: the number of muscles ^{4}_____ to say a single word

30,000: the number of people ^{5}_____ each year by cobras and vipers

> suffer   send   make   start   arrive

NUMBERS: Machines

40: the percentage of spam email ^{6}_____ at addresses ^{7}_____ with A, M, S, R or P

53: the percentage of people ^{8}_____ from nomophobia (fear of being without their cells)

100: the number of cars ^{9}_____ every minute

14,528: the number of text messages ^{10}_____ by a California girl in one month

VOCABULARY PLUS TWO-PART PHRASES

9 Correct the mistake in each two-part phrase.

           quiet
1 I only wanted peace and ~~downs~~, and what did I get? A screaming baby!

2 Our relationship has its ups and bounds, but I'd say we're a solid couple.

3 You have to weigh up the leaps and cons and then decide.

4 There's some back and take in every friendship; don't be so selfish.

5 I'm sick and ready of your complaints. Shut up or leave!

6 We could go off and on about this forever, let's just end the conversation now.

7 We only meet rough and then, but that's enough for me.

8 Our business was going nowhere, now it's improving by leaps and don'ts.

FUNCTION GIVING A TOUR

10 A Add vowels to complete the words and phrases.

a) h_ _d _v_r
b) w_rth
c) m_d_l_d
d) _pp_r_ntly
e) b_rned
f) m_y kn_w
g) n_m_d
h) r_tr_c_
i) b_l__v_
j) s_pp_s_dly
k) f__nd_d
l) st_ry g__s

10 B Use words and phrases a)–f) to complete part 1 of the tour and g)–k) to complete part 2.

Tour of Kyoto, Japan, part 1

The original city of Kyoto was ^{1}_____ on the ancient Chinese capital Chang'an. Many buildings were ^{2}_____ down in the 15th-century Onin War, but the city survived the Second World War. As you ^{3}_____, Kyoto is famous for its geisha. ^{4}_____ women who train to be geisha today are not allowed to marry or have cell phones. The two famous geisha districts, Gion and Pontocho, are well ^{5}_____ a visit, so let's ^{6}_____ there later.

Tour of Kyoto, Japan, part 2

Here we are at the Jishu shrine. See those two stones? The ^{7}_____ that if you walk from one to the other, you will one day find true love. And this is Kiyomizu-dera temple, which was ^{8}_____ in 798. It's ^{9}_____ after a waterfall nearby. ^{10}_____ it or not, not one nail was used to build it. Why don't we ^{11}_____ our steps to the Manga Museum— ^{12}_____ they have over 200,000 titles and we can read as many manga as we want.

REVIEW 4: UNITS 9–10   R5

CHECK

Circle the correct option to complete the sentences.

1. Her performance was _____, but otherwise the play was rather disappointing.
   a) outstanding   b) controversial   c) touching

2. That's strange, I remember _____ this letter, but here it is in my bag.
   a) mail   b) mailing   c) to mail

3. He was _____ for identity theft.
   a) suspected   b) arrested   c) saved

4. My best _____ lives in Paris, works in advertising.
   a) friend who   b) friend, whose   c) friend, who

5. There was so much _____ about the new show that it was sure to be a _____.
   a) hype, letdown   b) rave reviews, flop
   c) ground-breaking, sell-out

6. The movie theater burned to the ground. Police think it was _____.
   a) hacking   b) mugging   c) arson

7. He _____ committed the murder. He wasn't even in the country at the time.
   a) may have   b) can't have   c) mustn't have

8. They'll need to _____ the canal if wider boats are going to sail through it.
   a) broaden   b) lengthen   c) deepen

9. It didn't _____ my mind to call you.
   a) catch   b) occur to   c) cross

10. She was eager to _____ her husband of the crime.
    a) clear   b) blame   c) save

11. I can't believe you _____ that guy who was _____ a tourist.
    a) deceived, snatching   b) were taken in, posing as
    c) were fooled by, pretending to be

12. That's the woman _____ son hit my son.
    a) who   b) whose   c) who's

13. Here we are at the president's childhood home. _____ it has two floors, and all the other houses around here have one.
    a) Interestingly   b) Supposedly   c) Apparently

14. I don't think it would have been a _____ if it hadn't created such a _____.
    a) must-see, mainstream   b) sell-out, stir
    c) flop, ground-breaking

15. She took her umbrella, _____ that it would rain at some point during the day.
    a) expected   b) expecting   c) having expected

16. The monument was modeled _____ a well-known ancient Egyptian obelisk.
    a) by   b) for   c) on

17. People _____ off by the economic crisis were happy to get any kind of job.
    a) lay   b) laid   c) laying

18. The protestors were _____ from marching through downtown without permission.
    a) accused   b) charged   c) banned

19. I really didn't hear you ring the doorbell. I _____ been sleeping, or maybe I was listening to music.
    a) could have   b) can't have   c) mightn't have

20. They seemed _____ if they were just having fun.
    a) to be   b) like   c) as

21. He _____ my wallet and _____ it for an identical one, which he gave back to me.
    a) grabbed, switched   b) swapped, snatched
    c) fooled, posed

22. Her first relationship was the one thing _____ she thought more than anything else.
    a) which   b) which about   c) about which

23. My foot got _____ in a hole, and I couldn't get it out.
    a) run over   b) stuck   c) locked out

24. Look, footprints! Someone _____ gotten here before us.
    a) could have   b) might have   c) must have

25. _____ all his life to build his dream house, he decided to travel instead.
    a) Having worked   b) Working   c) Worked

26. A search engine is a good _____ tool for checking spelling.
    a) off-and-on   b) rough-and-ready
    c) now-and-then

27. We stopped on the way up the mountain _____ a break.
    a) to take   b) taking   c) take

28. The pill's working, and my headache's beginning _____.
    a) going   b) go   c) to go

29. The book was so _____ that I couldn't put it down.
    a) touching   b) creepy   c) fast-paced

30. My first girlfriend knew me _____, and no one has understood me as well since.
    a) through and through   b) off and on
    c) ups and downs

RESULTS /30

AUDIO SCRIPTS

UNIT 1 RECORDING W1.1

1 I wonder if you could introduce us to the director.
2 Do you mind me asking how much your camera cost?
3 Would you mind telling me what you do exactly?
4 I'd like to know whether it's really worth upgrading to the new smartphone.
5 Can you tell me which platform the Eurostar train leaves from?
6 What do you think he'll do when he discovers the mistake?

UNIT 1 RECORDING W1.2

I = Interviewer, O = Owen Winters

I: Do you have a dream? Is there something you've always wanted to do but somehow have never managed to? Well my guest today is the man who can make it all happen, for a price of course, Owen Winters, founder of Dreams Come True. Owen, welcome to the program.
O: Thank you for having me.
I: So, tell us, how does Dreams Come True work?
O: OK, well it's pretty simple. We help people make their lifelong dream come true—whatever it is.
I: So, if I, for instance, have dreamed of being a rock star since I was a teenager, you can help me with that.
O: Yes, that's right. And, in fact, not long ago we had a client, a woman, who wanted exactly that.
I: And you made her a rock star.
O: Well, we couldn't give her talent ...
I: Not that rock stars are always talented.
O: Right, but in talking with her, we worked out that the image she had in her mind was doing a live concert to a huge audience. She wanted to experience the sensation of performing in front of thousands of screaming fans.
I: And, so, how did you manage that?
O: Well, to be honest, it's a bit like producing a scene in a movie. In fact, that's my background; I worked as a production manager in the movie business for many years, till just a few years ago.
I: That's interesting.
O: Yeah, so in this case, we needed to find a venue, an arena where rock concerts are held, a place we could rent out for an evening. Then we needed a backing band, a crew to set the whole thing up and ...
I: And how about the thousands of screaming fans?
O: Well, just like getting extras for a movie, it's not that difficult.
I: Did you pay the fans?
O: Some of them, yes. We cost out the different parts of the plan, write a budget, give the client the figure, and, if they agree to the terms, we go ahead and do it.
I: How much did this rock concert cost?
O: I'm afraid I can't tell you. We don't reveal any financial details.
I: Oh, OK. Well, what other dreams have you made come true recently?
O: Let's see, we've just finished working with a client who wants to fly across the Atlantic Ocean on a supersonic airplane.
I: But Concorde no longer flies.
O: No, but we've just found a solution to that, using an air force plane. I can't tell you which air force.
I: Another trade secret.
O: Well, a military secret, actually. And another client wants to pilot a submarine. We've done the Normandy beach landings from the Second World War, with the client as general; we've done dining with a movie star, spending a night inside a pyramid and lots of make-up jobs.
I: Make-up jobs?
O: Yes, some people—all their life—have been curious about what it's like to be a man or a woman, or a celebrity ...
I: And you make them up to look the way they want.
O: That's right. We've recently done a job for a guy who wanted to look like Tom Cruise for a day. Our make-up artist did a great job, but the guy couldn't wait for the day to end.
I: Why was that?
O: Too much attention. He couldn't go anywhere without getting asked for an autograph. We suggested that we provide bodyguards, but he didn't want to pay for that.
I: And have you ever had to say no to a request?
O: Hmm ... We never say no to a dream. But sometimes it does take time. One client wanted to fly in space, to be an astronaut. That wasn't possible back when she first requested it. But, since then, it's become possible for ordinary people to go into space, again for a price, and, in fact, she's blasting off on the next tourist flight.
I: Incredible. So what do you think has been your most extraordinary request? And ...

UNIT 1 RECORDING W1.3

1 a/b I'd like to inquire about a reservation I made.
2 a/b I was wondering if that would be possible.
3 a/b Would there be any chance of getting the same price for the following weekend?
4 a/b I'd be really grateful if you could make an exception.
5 a/b Would you mind telling me why it's so complicated to change?
6 a/b Do you mind me asking what your name is?
7 a/b Would you mind transferring me to your supervisor?

UNIT 1 RECORDING W1.4

A: Eden Gardens Hotel. How can I help you?
B: Hi, I'd like to inquire about a reservation I made. The reservation reference is 6714.
A: OK. How can I help you?
B: I need to change the dates to one week later. I was wondering if that would be possible and how much the change will cost.
A: Let me just check. Ah, it's a two-for-one weekend deal.
B: Yes. Would there be any chance of getting the same price for the following weekend?
A: I'm not sure. Bear with me a minute.
B: I'd be really grateful if you could make an exception.
A: I need to ask my supervisor. Can you just hold on a minute? I'll just see.
B: OK.
A: Sorry to keep you. No, sorry, we can't do that.
B: I have one more question, if I'm not keeping you. Would you mind telling me why it's so complicated to change?
A: Sorry, it's policy. Online special deals are non-refundable, non-transferable.
B: Do you mind me asking what your name is?
A: We aren't allowed to give our full names.
B: In that case, would you mind transferring me to your supervisor.

UNIT 2 RECORDING W2.1

1 domestic   5 global
2 economic   6 industrial
3 urban   7 ethical
4 political   8 rural

UNIT 2 RECORDING W2.2

1 She's done all her homework.
   She's been doing her homework since she got home from school.
2 I've sent 25 application letters this morning.
   I've been sending application letters all morning. I need a break!
3 Pete called and left you a message.
   Pete's been calling you all evening. Is your cell on?
4 I've read this magazine. Do you want to borrow it?
   I've been reading this magazine. Do you want to borrow it when I've finished?

5 Julia's gone to the gym—do you want me to ask her to call you back?
Julia's been going to the gym and she's ten pounds lighter now.
6 The temperature has dropped to minus 30.
The temperature has been dropping all day.

UNIT 2 RECORDING W2.3

Speaker 1
I decided to do this because I hate it when people forget my name. Like at school, the teachers who don't know your name, they don't give you so much attention. So, anyway, I looked on some websites to find out the best way to do it. Apparently there are two important things: first is that, when you're introduced, you really pay attention and look at the person and try to find a way to remember the name. For example, I recently met a woman called Keira, and she had curly hair: so Keira, curly, sound similar, you see what I mean? That was easy. Then, second, you need to repeat the name as often as possible, say it to yourself several times and use it when you're talking to the person. You just have to be careful that you don't sound really strange. Anyway, the result's been good. Somehow people seem friendlier, and I feel a lot more confident about chatting to people. The only problem is someone told me it made people uncomfortable because they couldn't remember my name!

Speaker 2
It was really difficult at first. ... I mean, you actually have to stop people trying to give you one. I didn't realize before I started how many are given out all the time. I thought this was a good thing to do because apparently it can take up to a thousand years for one to decay, and about 13 billion are given out each year in the UK alone. And it's not only the pollution, but also animals and fish can get caught in them. Anyway, I invested in two shopping bags, and I've been using them for the past three months. The only problem is I keep forgetting to take them out of the house or I leave them in the car, which is very annoying. My solution has been to get one of those fold-up bags that you can carry in your pocket or bag. I've gotten all my friends to do the same, and now our local stores are going to become a plastic-bag-free zone. At least that will make me remember to take a bag!

Speaker 3
I thought this was a good one to try because everyone always looks so bored or miserable, especially on public transportation. So, the next time I was sitting on a train and someone sat across from me, I looked up and gave them a big smile. They looked a bit surprised but smiled back at me, then buried their face in the newspaper. I got the impression they were a bit embarrassed. Anyway, I continued and kept smiling at all sorts of people during the day. To be honest, I got a mixed reaction, but the kids and older people seemed the friendliest. Oh, and I found out later that one woman in the office thought I was flirting with her!

Speaker 4
I decided to combine two of the ideas. I've always been hopeless at telling jokes. I'm sure it's not because I don't have a sense of humor. It's something about the timing. And I know that jokes are great for building relationships and good for me personally because I often have to give business presentations, and a funny story really helps build rapport with the audience. One of the best things about doing this was that I asked all my friends to tell me their favorite jokes, and we had lots of laugh-out-loud times together. And I'm getting better, though I did have one very embarrassing moment at work when I told my joke to my boss and he just stared at me like I was an idiot. You want to hear a joke? Something short? OK … uh, What do cows do on Saturday night? They rent mooooovies!

UNIT 2 RECORDING W2.4

1 In the 2008 Olympics, Usain Bolt set three world records, including the 100 meters.
2 If you stay in Spain for more than 90 days, you need to apply for a resident's permit.
3 CCTV cameras have been successful, with a huge decrease in incidents of violence.
4 Police have launched a nationwide appeal for help to find a missing 16-year-old.
5 The National Gallery is planning to project gigantic images of Picasso paintings onto the outside of the building.
6 The Water for You scheme is a project to give hundreds of people access to clean water.
7 Researchers recorded South American river turtles talking to each other underwater.
8 The amount of ice at the South Pole has decreased significantly over the last ten years.
9 Students are permitted to work and study in this country.
10 Environmentalists appealed to supermarkets to reduce the amount of food waste.

UNIT 2 RECORDING W2.5

A: Do you think students should be allowed to use their phones in class?
B: Yeah, I'm in favor of that. The way I see it is that students would be more motivated if they could use phones, maybe to make short movies or things like that.
A: Mm, I'm not so sure. You know how kids are. It seems to me that they'd just start texting each other whenever they were bored.
B: Mm, well, I agree to a certain extent. They would certainly need very strict rules, you know, about turning them on and off. But phones could be useful for things like practicing languages or setting homework reminders.
A: Yes, I suppose so, but what about bullying, you know, kids sending each other nasty messages? Or phones could be a target for thieves.
B: Fair enough, but either of those things could happen after school.
A: Hmm. I see your point, but I'm still not convinced. I think, on balance, it's better to keep them out of classes.
B: I disagree. I think we should encourage them.

UNIT 2 RECORDING W2.6

I'm in favor of that.
I'm not so sure. It seems to me that
I agree to a certain extent.
I suppose so.
Fair enough, but …
I see your point, but I'm … I'm still not convinced.
I disagree.

UNIT 2 RECORDING W2.7

illegal, reasonable, unethical, disturbing, outrageous, irresponsible

R1 RECORDING R1.1

1 authority, nervous, awkward
2 identify, crime, relieved
3 outrageous, information, decrease
4 witty, permit, disappointing
5 non-refundable, urban, frustrated

R1 RECORDING R1.2

A group of rock stars is appealing for people to fund a new project aimed at preventing malaria. Recent medical research shows there is a dramatic decrease in the disease when malaria nets are provided for families.
Fifty-two tourists have been rescued from the desert near the Step Pyramid in Egypt after temperatures reached 49 degrees Celsius—the highest level ever recorded in the area. The tourists were stranded when their bus broke down. The group's tour operator has been arrested for failing to obtain a permit to conduct business in the area and has been ordered to pay a fine.
And, in business, a number of European countries are planning to cut imports from the United States as trade tensions continue. The USA has recently increased taxes on produce coming from abroad to an all-time high.

AUDIO SCRIPTS

R1 RECORDING R1.3

1 appealing
2 project
3 research
4 decrease
5 desert
6 recorded
7 permit
8 fine
9 imports
10 produce

UNIT 3 RECORDING W3.1

An eight-year-old boy has been rescued by an enterprising Bangkok firefighter. The boy from Thailand is autistic and had been feeling very nervous before his first day of school, but initially he seemed to be OK. However, during the first lesson, his teacher was explaining something to the class when she realized that the boy had climbed out of the window. "He was sitting just outside the window with his legs swinging over the edge."

The rescue services were called in when the boy's mother had also failed to get the boy down. Everyone was beginning to run out of ideas when one of the firefighters, Somchai Yoosabai, overheard the boy's mother talking about her son's love of superheroes. The quick-thinking fireman rushed back to the fire station and changed into his Spider-Man costume. (Until then, Mr. Somchai had been using the costume to make school fire drills more interesting.) "I told him 'Spider-Man is here to rescue you. No monsters are going to attack you.'" The sight brought a smile to the youngster's face, and he immediately walked into his rescuer's arms.

UNIT 3 RECORDING W3.2

Hello and welcome to *Arts Review*. In tonight's program, we look at a rather surprising answer to the question: How many stories exist? You might think that there are hundreds or thousands of different stories in literature, theater and movies, but experts like to put the number somewhat lower, anything between one and twelve. Now, in a new book, Christopher Booker says that there are exactly seven basic "plots," and every story in the world can fit into one of them. Before we review his book, here are the seven.

Plot one: Overcoming the monster.
In this story, the hero or heroine has to battle and defeat a monster. This could be a real monster, for example, Dracula, or it could be a person, such as a villain in a James Bond movie. The monster is defeated, the hero is victorious, the community is saved, and order returns to the world. Most detective stories are actually variations on the theme of overcoming the monster.

Plot two: Rags to riches.
This idea is found in countless stories. It involves a very ordinary person or someone that everyone thinks is normal, nothing special. Then, during the course of the story, it's shown that this person is in fact extraordinary. Just think of the story of Superman or any story of an ordinary person who ends up marrying someone rich.

Plot three: The quest.
This features a main character who travels a long distance, often with companions, in search of a treasure or to do a brave or noble act. At the end, he or she succeeds and is rewarded in some way, often by keeping the treasure or sometimes by saving a community. Probably the best known example of this is *The Lord of the Rings*. Interestingly, it's also often the basis of many computer games.

Plot four: Voyage and return.
This typically tells the story of an ordinary person who is thrown into a completely strange and alien world, one that is outside their experience. Often they face dangers and difficulties and then have a thrilling escape back to their original situation. There was a TV series called *Lost* about people whose plane crashed on a desert island. That was a voyage and return story.

Plot five: Comedy.
This doesn't always mean humor, although the story can be funny. It's more about a situation that is full of mistakes and mix-ups. The whole story gets more and more confused until, at the end, everything is sorted out and there's a happy ending.

Plot six: Tragedy.
As its name suggests, this plot never has a happy ending. It's about what terrible things can happen when someone tries to get power or go against the system. This person often has a weakness in their character, and this weakness is the reason that everything ends badly. There are lots of examples in theater, such as Romeo and Juliet, who fall in love although their families hate each other.

Plot seven: Rebirth.
This plot is about a person in a dark and difficult situation, maybe they've lost all their money or their job or they are in prison. Or perhaps he or she is unpopular or has an unpleasant personality. Then a series of events happens, often amazing events, and the situation or the person changes so that the character becomes a kind of hero, a very positive character.

So that's all seven. Before we go onto discuss these, there's an interesting quote from the American novelist, Kurt Vonnegut, who claimed …

UNIT 3 RECORDING W3.3

1 I wish I'd had more money.
2 I wish you'd worked harder at school.
3 I wish it would stop raining.
4 If only we'd told her.
5 If only we'd gone to the party.
6 If only you'd turned it off.

UNIT 3 RECORDING W3.4

Conversation 1
A: What did you think of the book?
B: Well, I'm not a big fan of travel books.
A: Oh, why's that?
B: I just couldn't get into all the description.

Conversation 2
A: I hear Nick's enjoying his new school.
B: Yes, what he loves about it is that they do a lot of sports.
A: I didn't know he liked sports.
B: Oh, yeah. He's really into football at the moment.

Conversation 3
A: Why don't you like barbecues?
B: I can't stand it when the meat isn't cooked properly.

UNIT 3 RECORDING W3.5

1 Well, I'm not a big fan of travel books.
2 I just couldn't get into all the description.
3 Yes, what he loves about it is they do a lot of sports.
4 Oh, yeah. He's really into football at the moment.
5 I can't stand it when the meat isn't cooked properly.

UNIT 4 RECORDING W4.1

Speaker 1
I'm logged on twenty-four hours a day, and, each time a message comes in, I check it … I start getting frustrated if I don't get at least one an hour. Nowadays, I often don't answer the phone when my old friends call. Almost all my friends are people I've met online. The other day I met some people I knew from college and I actually found it really strange talking to them face to face because I'm much more used to interacting with people online. I'm a bit worried because my eyes are starting to hurt really badly …

Speaker 2
It's the quizzes and other applications that get me, like there's always a new questionnaire or test for something, you know, "Do your friends think you're cool?" or "How long would you survive on a desert island?" Then there's Farmville, you know, where you have to manage a farm—I've been doing that for the last two months. Now I can't stop thinking about it. I lie in bed at night planning what I'll do when I log on next time. So of course, I'm not …

Speaker 3
When I was in high school, I was completely hooked. I used to sit in class checking my texts, and sometimes I told the teacher I was sick so I could go outside and log on to chat with friends. I would often skip lunch so I could keep on chatting. I spent more time online than I did studying, so then my grades went down …

AUDIO SCRIPTS

Speaker 4
I realized it was getting ridiculous when my daughter actually sent me a message through Facebook asking for help with her homework ... I mean, she was only in the next room! To be fair, she probably asked me in person first, but I suppose I'd gotten so absorbed in the site that I didn't hear her. I'm also not taking real care of myself—I have terrible headaches all the time. I know you're supposed to stop and give yourself a break regularly, but I never remember. Anyway, after that ...

Speaker 5
I lost my job because of it. It started out that I'd just go onto the website during coffee breaks, but then I started to log on during work time. When a chat message came in, I couldn't resist. I'd stop what I was doing and join the conversation ... and my boss noticed that I was working less and less. He warned me a couple of times ... then he fired me. So then I ...

UNIT 4   RECORDING W4.2

1 I used to love it.
2 I didn't use to discuss it.
3 We'd always eat together.
4 We'd always argue.
5 He's not used to it yet.
6 They'll be in the park.
7 I was always getting into trouble.
8 He'll be at the office.

UNIT 4   RECORDING W4.3

Basically, the way it works is that you draw a grid of 5 by 5 squares on a piece of paper. There are two players, and the aim of the game is to complete the sequence "SOS" in a straight line as many times as you can. So, the first thing you do is one of you writes an "S" or an "O" in one of the squares. Then the other player writes an "S" or an "O" in another square. Whenever one of you completes an "SOS," you get another turn, and the point is not to let your partner succeed because what happens is that one player gets an "SOS" and then blocks the other player. It's easy to lose track of who's winning, so the key thing is to keep score of who gets how many "SOS"s. Then, after you've finished (once the grid is full), the winner is the player with the most "SOS"s.

UNIT 4   RECORDING W4.4

1 Look up the idiom where?
2 I should see whom?
3 You last spoke to her when?
4 I can use a question word to do what?
5 Who's waiting backstage?
6 The rain's doing what?
7 I'll find you where?
8 The what's too high?

R2   RECORDING R2.1

1 biography, wind up, chill
2 pick up, inspiring, lyrics
3 brought up, autobiography, drop out
4 hilarious, focus on, grow up
5 wikipedia, recharge, delightful
6 get on, switch off, moving

UNIT 5   RECORDING W5.1

A: Have you ever wondered why pregnant women don't tip over? Why woodpeckers don't get headaches? Or why, if you bend a piece of dry spaghetti, it often breaks into three or more pieces? Well, researchers have studied questions like these, and some of these researchers have received the so-called Ig Nobel Prize for their work. And here to talk to us about the prize is Martha Anton. So, Martha, what is the Ig Nobel Prize and what's your connection to it?
B: Well, the name of the prize is, of course, a play on words—it's not the Nobel, it's the Ig-Nobel, as in *ignoble*—and it's awarded to researchers and inventors for doing work that first makes you laugh, then makes you think.
A: So it's not a serious award.
B: Well, yes and no. Sometimes it's given to someone as a criticism of their work, sometimes as humor, but, in many cases, the prize goes to someone for doing something that we might think is really silly or trivial, but that might lead to a major breakthrough. Some of the most important discoveries in history started with a joke. And at the awards ceremony, actual winners of the Nobel Prize present the Ig Nobel Prizes.
A: And what's your connection with the Ig Nobel Prize?
B: Besides the fact that I've always been a big fan of the prize and fascinated by the sort of people who win it, I'm hoping to win it myself.
A: I'd like to ask you about that in a minute. So what other research has won the Ig Nobel?
B: Well, two researchers in Newcastle won the Veterinary Medicine prize for showing that if you give a cow a name and use the name, it will give more milk.
A: Fascinating.
B: And there have been a great many inventions, for example, a teenager repellent.
A: A teenager repellent?
B: Yes, it's a device that makes an annoying noise that only teenagers can hear.
A: So adults can use it to keep teenagers away.
B: That's right.
A: I can't imagine why they'd want to do that.
B: Well, actually it was developed and it's been used by storeowners who want to stop teenagers hanging around outside their stores.
A: Really?
B: And then there's the alarm clock that runs away and hides so that people can't switch it off and go back to sleep.
A: Incredible!
B: That won the Ig Nobel for Economics, because it helps add more work hours to the day.
A: Naturally.
B: Oh, yes, some years ago, two Japanese researchers won the prize for their device called the Bow-Lingual. It translates from dog talk to human talk.
A: The Bow-Lingual. I get it.
B: And a Korean won for inventing a business suit that automatically perfumes itself.
A: So that a businessperson doesn't walk into a meeting smelling bad.
B: My favorite though was the washing machine for dogs and cats.
A: That would work perfectly with the Bow-Lingual. So what is your invention?
B: It's research, actually, into whether it's better to walk or run in the rain. If you don't have an umbrella, that is.
A: Hm. Which way you get less wet, you mean.
B: Yes, that's right.
A: And so which is better?
B: Ummm ... I'm afraid we haven't finished the research yet. Give me another six months of bad weather, and we'll have the answer!

UNIT 5   RECORDING W5.2

adjust to, damage, access, transform, effect, revolutionize, devastating, positive, enable, do harm to, adapt to

UNIT 5   RECORDING W5.3

A: What do you think about simply writing the rule on a sign on the wall: "English only"?
B: I think it's too simple. We'd ignore it.
C: How do you feel about a fine system? You have to pay if you speak your language.
B: That could be a problem. Not everyone has money for fines.
A: Suppose we try a mother-tongue "island." A place in the room where you can go to speak your mother tongue if you really need to.
C: That's not a bad idea.
B: It wouldn't work. Everyone would be on the island!
A: Would you consider having five-minute mother-tongue breaks in the middle of the lesson?
B: I think we're on the wrong track here. It's either punishment or reward, nothing else works.

AUDIO SCRIPTS

C: How does giving a prize for using only English strike you? Like no homework? Or chocolate?
B: Should we go for that?
A: It'd be great if we could get more nationalities in the group. Then we'd naturally speak English more.
B: It wouldn't be my first choice. Where are we going to find these people?
C: I'm torn between punishment and reward systems—fines or prizes.
A: Could we go for both?
B: Yeah, let's go with that.

UNIT 5   RECORDING W5.4

1 bizarre
2 predictable
3 criticizing
4 coming up with
5 rejected
6 dreadful
7 unrealistic
8 brilliant

UNIT 5   RECORDING W5.5

1 To be honest, I thought your first suggestion was better.
2 To put it bluntly, that's the worst idea I've heard today.
3 Actually, I don't think that's a very practical idea.
4 Frankly, it's just not going to work.
5 I have to say, that's probably the only way.

UNIT 6   RECORDING W6.1

Speaker 1
I don't think there's any quick and easy rule, so, for me, any time is the right time. I began when I was six, but, then again, I knew someone who started when they were almost fifty, and she's still going strong now she's over seventy. You're never too old. I suppose the key is how much time you have to practice and your motivation. My parents let me try out different instruments, and eventually I chose the violin. That's important, too. I'm not sure my parents were too happy about my choice, though! They had to put up with years of me sounding like a dying cat!

Speaker 2
I think there's actually a legal minimum age in some countries, something like 35, but in my opinion it should be at least 50. Otherwise you just don't have enough experience to do it. But, then, of course, you have to strike a balance between maturity and energy. You need to be able to react quickly to events and survive sometimes on very little sleep. So, yes, someone in their 50s or maybe 60s could manage, but no older than that.

Speaker 3
I couldn't really give a number at all, since I can't state what's right for other people. I think it has to do with giving yourself enough time to get to know yourself and to understand your relationship together well enough so that neither of you will create an unhealthy environment for the child. Some people say there's never a right time, but I think there's definitely a wrong time—too soon.

Speaker 4
Lots of people I know didn't know what they wanted to do with their life when they were 20, and they still don't know now they're over 40! But seriously, it's OK to decide young, if you have a real vocation, you know, you've always wanted to be a doctor or an engineer or something like that. But most of us don't have much idea when we leave school. So I reckon the best idea is to try out lots of things to see what you enjoy and develop lots of general skills. That worked for me. Most companies need staff who can get along with other people and can communicate their ideas clearly and who have reasonable computer skills and things like that.

UNIT 6   RECORDING W6.2

unrealistic
unfamiliar, unpredictable
dissatisfied, illogical, irrelevant
impatient, immortal, unwilling, unhealthy
misbehave, insecure
misinterpret

UNIT 6   RECORDING W6.3

1
A: Look at this picture. Isn't it time they banned "size zero" models?
B: Well, clothes do look really good on them.
A: But it sends a terrible message to young girls. Shouldn't they know it isn't normal to be so skinny?
B: I've never really thought about it much.
A: Well you should. Clearly, these images add to the pressure on young girls.
B: Yeah, you're probably right.
2
A: Don't you think that they should use technology in football games?
B: What, you mean instead of referees?
A: Yeah, to make decisions. Anyone can see it would be fairer.
B: But you need referees for all sorts of reasons.
A: Yeah, but surely it's more important that decisions are correct.
B: Hmm. I suppose you have a point.

UNIT 6   RECORDING W6.4

A: Look at this picture. Isn't it time they banned "size zero" models?
A: But it sends a terrible message to young girls. Shouldn't they know it isn't normal to be so skinny?
A: Well you should. Clearly, these images add to the pressure on young girls.
A: Don't you think that they should use technology in football games?
A: Yeah, to make decisions. Anyone can see it would be fairer.
A: Yeah, but surely it's more important that decisions are correct.

UNIT 6   RECORDING W6.5

1
A: Do you like this dress on me?
B: I prefer the white one.
A: So what you're saying is, this one, which cost a fortune, looks terrible.
B: No, I mean the white one makes you look slimmer.
A: So, in other words, I look fat!
B: No, no, you're twisting my words. I just meant that you look *even* slimmer in the white one.
2
A: Don't you think we should pay a decorator to do it?
B: So, basically, you think I can't do it.
A: I didn't mean that. It's just that it might be quicker and save us money.
B: So, what you mean is that I might mess it up.
A: No, but you're a perfectionist, and you know how long it takes you to do things.
B: So, you'd rather spend money and end up with a worse job!
A: Not exactly …

UNIT 7   RECORDING W7.1

Speaker 1
One of my favorite programs when I was a kid was a very famous show called *Mister Benn*. I don't really remember that much about it. I know it was my favorite because my mother tells me it was. It was a cartoon, and, from what I remember, it's about a guy who goes into a fancy clothes store and he puts on a different outfit and then, every time he comes out of the clothes store, he's then transported to a world that corresponds with the outfit that he's wearing. I think I liked it because there was this innocent sense of adventure about it. I can't remember much about any individual episodes though.

Speaker 2
The classic for Brits of my generation is *Blue Peter*—it's hard to underestimate its cultural impact. It was a kind of magazine program for children. Basically, it involved two or three hosts (who also had a dog and a cat) involved

AUDIO SCRIPTS

in various tasks—demonstrating how to make toys or ornaments out of everyday household objects, short documentary trips to various places of interest and so on. Occasionally they held interviews with famous actors or performers of some sort. They would also bring in people who had some form of talent—musical, for example—to do live studio performances. Everyone wanted a "Blue Peter badge," the special prize you could be awarded if you wrote in and they read your letter or if you won a competition or something similar—literally a badge of honor.

Speaker 3
I liked this show *Grange Hill* because it was, I think, an accurate representation of what life in an English middle school in a British city is like, and it dealt with issues that were interesting for teen ... perhaps a bit younger than teenagers ... So, like when you were from nine to twelve. I think it was a really good show because you're not yet old enough to watch adult TV, but you're too old to watch kids' TV, and it kind of bridges the gap between the two, and it deals with issues like drugs and sex in a non-patronizing, non-condescending way. I suppose it was a kind of soap opera for kids, but a pretty serious one.

Speaker 4
When I was a teenager, my favorite show was *Monty Python*. It was different from any other kind of comedy show we'd had before. Instead of separate sketches with proper endings, in *Monty Python* they'd start a sketch and then suddenly stop it halfway, or one sketch would morph into another. If a sketch was getting boring, there'd be a news announcer coming on and saying "and now for something completely different!" The links between the sketches would sometimes be cartoons, very surrealistic and weird cartoons of people exploding or strange machines. I suppose one of the main reasons I liked it was because my parents didn't understand it at all, so it was a kind of rebellion. After a Monty Python night, we'd spend our entire lunch break at school going through it, remembering all the catchphrases and taking each sketch apart.

UNIT 7 RECORDING W7.2

1 If I say something offensive, I'm often too stubborn to take it back.
2 If a homeless person knocked on my door in the middle of winter, I would put them up for the night.
3 Hard work brings out the best in me.
4 I come across as being more sociable than I really am.
5 If it turned out that my partner had lied to me, I would be disappointed in him.

UNIT 7 RECORDING W7.3

A: This is totally outrageous. Your questions are very biased against the government. I've never heard such biased statements from a journalist before. Absolutely incredible.
B: Well, minister, you're the one who's always telling the people that we're getting richer when the cost of living is increasing and our wages are staying the same. How on earth do you justify that?
A: Look, there's no way I'd say that if the data didn't agree! Having said that, I do think we can do better to help ordinary people, and, so, we're going to cut gasoline tax.
B: That is a good idea, minister, but why are you introducing it now? Is it because the election is in two months?
A: That is so wrong! Are you suggesting that we're making up policies to gain votes?
B: To be honest minister, the amazing thing is that you're denying making policies to win votes.

UNIT 7 RECORDING W7.4

A: This is totally outrageous.
A: Absolutely incredible.
B: you're the one who's always telling the people that we're getting richer ...
B: How on earth do you justify that?
A: Look, there's no way I'd say that if the data didn't agree!
A: Having said that, I do think we can do better to help ordinary people
B: That is a good idea, minister, but why are you introducing it now?
A: That is so wrong!
B: the amazing thing is that you're denying making policies to win votes.

UNIT 8 RECORDING W8.1

Part 1
Today, in the third of my lectures on human behavior, I'm going to talk about the difference between the way people act when they're being watched—or think they're being watched—and how they act when they're unobserved. I'll be describing a recent experiment conducted at Newcastle University. I'll be drawing conclusions from this experiment, to see what it teaches us about psychology and behavior, and, finally, I'll be comparing it with other key research findings in the area.
So, what did the team at Newcastle set out to discover? They wanted to find out whether the simple belief that they were being watched would alter people's behavior. To do this, they made use of an "honesty box" in a staff common room at the university. The idea behind the honesty box was that staff members would pay the correct amount for their coffee and tea. This honesty box had been in there for several years, so no one had any idea that an experiment was taking place.
What they did was to place a small poster at eye-level above the honesty box, listing the prices for the drinks. However, each week the poster alternated between different images of either flowers or of a pair of eyes looking straight at the observer. Here, you can see examples of the kind of pictures they used. At the end of each week, the team monitored the amount of money that had been collected and compared this to the volume of milk that had been consumed. They found that people paid nearly three times as much money when the notice included a pair of eyes as when it included an image of flowers.

UNIT 8 RECORDING W8.2

Part 2
So what does this experiment tell us? Well, first, it underlines something we already know—that our brains are hard-wired, are programed, to respond to faces and eyes. It's important for people to know if they're being watched. Second, it shows that people are influenced if they think they're being watched; they behave less selfishly. The team was surprised by the significant difference in the findings.
And what implications could this have for the future? Well, the team believes the idea could be applied to public situations where people have to decide whether to behave well or badly. One example would be for warnings for speed cameras. The team's previous studies show that drivers would react more positively to images of faces and eyes than to a picture of a camera. Another place where a picture of eyes could be placed is near a CCTV camera downtowns.
Now, before I go on to discuss other studies, does anyone have any questions?

UNIT 8 RECORDING W8.3

1 What would you have done?
2 I wouldn't have done that.
3 If I'd known when you were coming, I would've met you at the station.

UNIT 8 RECORDING W8.4

A: Is everything OK?
B: Um, actually, there's something I've been meaning to talk to you about.
A: Oh, is there a problem?
B: I don't want you to get the wrong idea, but ...
A: That sounds bad.
B: It's just that you often leave your cell on.
A: I don't understand.
B: And it rings when you're not here, and that's annoying.
A: But I need to keep it on in case my son calls.

AUDIO SCRIPTS

B: Yes, but it's disturbing when people are trying to work.
A: It's important that he can get straight through to me.
B: I understand, but do you see where I'm coming from?
A: I suppose so.
B: Maybe you could set it to silent when you're not here.
A: What you mean just the "vibrate" setting?
B: Yes, how would you feel about that?
A: OK, that sounds reasonable. I'll do that from now on. Sorry about that.
B: Thanks, I'd appreciate it.

UNIT 8 RECORDING W8.5

1 Actually, there's something I've, um, been meaning to talk to you about.
2 Well, I don't want you to get the wrong idea, but …
3 It's just that, you know, you often leave your cell on …
4 And it rings when you're not here, and that's slightly annoying.
5 Yes, but it's a bit disturbing when people are trying to work.
6 I understand, but, I mean, do you see where I'm coming from?
7 Maybe you could just set it to silent when you're not here.
8 Yes, how would you er feel about that?

R4 RECORDING R4.1

1 biased, deny, promise
2 reality, threaten, sketch
3 serial, circulation, generosity
4 persuade, tabloid, sensationalism
5 focused, confrontational, control
6 sensible, aggressive, assess

UNIT 9 RECORDING W9.1

A: … and we're joined today by Alex Temple, a researcher in something called inattentional blindness. Welcome to the show.
B: Thank you.
A: So, for starters, can you tell us exactly what "inattentional blindness" is?
B: Well, the best way I can explain it is through some of the experiments that have been done. The most famous is the gorilla experiment. Subjects are shown a movie of two groups throwing around a basketball, one group dressed in white, the other in dark clothes. And the viewer is told to count the number of times the team in white passes the ball. After about ten seconds, someone dressed in a gorilla suit walks out to the middle, faces the camera and then walks off. Most people watching the movie don't notice the gorilla.

A: Don't notice it? That's hard to believe.
B: It seems that way till you do it. The point is that it's part of the nature of how we see, or don't see, when we pay attention.
A: You mean when we pay attention we see less.
B: When we pay attention we see what we're paying attention to. If I ask you to go out on Oxford Street and count the number of people with glasses, then when you come back I ask how many teenagers you saw with parrots on their shoulders, we'd get a similar result, even if there were several teenagers with parrots.
A: I suppose so. But why is this so important?

UNIT 9 RECORDING W9.2

B: Well, when this happens in everyday life, it can have significant consequences—a lot of accidents happen because of inattentional blindness.
A: For example?
B: Well, for example, road accidents. Many accidents happen when a driver is talking on his or her cell phone, using a hands-free set-up, which is legal. A driver in this situation actually misses a great deal of visual information or is slower to process it.
A: A car stopping in front of them for instance?
B: Exactly. When there's a smooth flow of traffic and the driver is talking on the phone, some of their ability to process visual information is taken away. A car stops in front of them, and it's like the gorilla—it's not what they're concentrating on, or looking for, and so they don't "see" it. They also tend not to notice billboards by the road, for instance, even really striking ones.
A: Maybe this explains why I miss signs when I'm driving.
B: Well, if you're driving in the USA and you're looking for a sign that says "city center," you might not notice the one that says "downtown," even if you're not talking on the phone. That's more about selective seeing, which is related to inattentional blindness.
A: And how is this … information used?
B: In lots of ways. We use simulators to demonstrate to trained pilots that they're less likely to notice something unusual on the airport runway than an untrained person—and this awareness helps them adjust how they use their visual perception and processing and can prevent accidents.
A: Fascinating.

B: And in more common jobs, like a guard in a store. They expect a thief to try and hide what they're doing, so, if someone steals something openly—just smiles, greets the guard and walks out of the store—they might not notice it. We do simulations to train guards not to be blinded by their expectations of how a thief behaves.
A: So it's really about training people not to be blind.
B: Yes. Though we've seen applications in design, too. It's happened that a car driver driving at night tried to overtake another car and simply didn't see the motorcycle coming in the other direction—because the headlights didn't look like car headlights. So some motorcycle headlights have been made to look more like car headlights.
A: Any advice for our listeners? Is this something they can use in everyday life?
B: Sure. Aside from not talking on the phone while driving, I'd say that it's important to be aware of how you're looking at things. How your expectations of what you'll see actually blinds you to what's there.
A: So, expect the unexpected?
B: Yes, exactly.

UNIT 9 RECORDING W9.3

1 It must have been you.
2 It couldn't have been me.
3 You may not have seen her.
4 They can't have been there.
5 We could have seen them.

UNIT 9 RECORDING W9.4

A: I've just been robbed, on the subway, by a pickpocket.
B: What happened?
A: Well, this guy got on the train, and he reminded me of that English soccer player … wait, my mind's gone blank. Oh, yeah, David Beckham.
B: David Beckham? Didn't you wonder why he was traveling on the subway?
A: It never occurred to me, no. Well, then everyone crowded around with their camera phones.
B: Typical!
A: I had to push my way past them, and, before I'd realized what was happening, my wallet was gone, right out of my bag.
B: Did you see or feel anyone take it?
A: No, in fact, it was only a minute later that I realized they'd done it. It all happened so fast, and I was in a hurry anyway.
B: So the David Beckham lookalike must have been a distraction.
A: Yeah, and he must have had someone working with him.
B: Well, the people with camera phones, maybe they …

AUDIO SCRIPTS

A: Do you think so? They seemed like students, but …
B: Oh, definitely, it was a pickpocket gang. That's how they work.

UNIT 9 RECORDING W9.5

A: It was a pretty bad accident. The front rim was completely twisted.
B: Rim?
A: The metal part of the wheel. And of course the spokes were broken.
B: Spokes?
A: The wires that go from the center of the wheel to the rim. The chain guard got dented.
B: Chain guard?
A: The metal thing that covers the chain. One pedal broke off.
B: Pedal?
A: The thing you put your foot on. And the handlebar got bent.
B: Handlebar?
A: The thing you hold when you ride. And somehow the seat got ripped.
B: Saddle?
A: The thing you sit on when you ride a bike.
B: Oh, dear. Did you break any bones?
A: Bones? I cracked my skull.
B: Skull?
A: That's the big bone inside your head.

UNIT 10 RECORDING W10.1

1 The people living on the other side of the river were trapped.
2 Anyone planning to go home early or wanting to take a break should let us know.
3 Walking out of the restaurant, I ran into my old boss coming in.
4 I used to work with the woman living next door.
5 I left the party quickly, not telling anyone that I was unwell.
6 Carrying a child under each arm, she ran out of the blazing building.
7 He jumped up, frightened by the loud bang, mistaking the door for a gun.
8 Walls painted white tend to attract more graffiti.

UNIT 10 RECORDING W10.2

Part 1

Hello everyone, and thank you for coming. This evening I'm going to talk to you about how to take great photographs—the five secrets that every good photographer knows and uses. To be honest, these aren't really secrets, but, hopefully, they'll be new to some of you, and you'll find them useful.
OK, let's start with a photograph that includes some of the most common mistakes that amateurs make … As you can see, this picture is a typical snapshot, the sort where someone got the woman to pose for the camera. Nothing against posing, though my preference is for more natural shots, but, in any case, there are several basic errors.
First of all, the picture-taker made sure the sun was behind him or her, to avoid sun going into the lens, and that's good, but this way the subject has the sun blasting on her face, just a flat hard light. It also means that she can't open her eyes properly!
Second, the subject has been centered in the frame, which leaves a lot of space at either side of her and creates a pretty boring and predictable image.
This leads me to the third common mistake that people make, which concerns the background. We can see too much background here—the street scene with parked cars is distracting and unattractive.
Fourth, overall there's too much space around the subject, the picture-taker is either too far away or has used the wrong perspective, or both. Leaving too much space around the subject can make them appear smaller than you'd like and make objects in the background too important.
The final thing to check is the angle. Amateur photographers often stand higher than their subject, which makes the subject look up—which is not the best angle to see a face, but … actually, in this case, the photographer has gotten it right and positioned the camera in line with the subject's eyes.
You might think I'm being unfair, since this is just a quick snapshot. But I want you to see just how simple it is to make even your family snapshots consistently good pictures.

UNIT 10 RECORDING W10.3

Part 2

OK, so here are the five key rules.
Rule number one: light from the side. So if you're outside, notice where the sun is shining from and position yourself so that it's to your left or right as you're facing your subject. If it's to your side, the subject won't have that flat hard light on them, but much more interesting shadows and shades, which give the image more depth and contour.
Rule number two is the rule of thirds. When you're framing a shot, divide the screen up into thirds both horizontally and vertically and think of the four points where the lines intersect as centers. If your subject is a face, position the face at one of these four points. In other words, place your subject off-center to add interest.
Which brings us to rule number three: think about your background. Avoid cluttered backgrounds, which distract from the main focus of your photograph. This may mean positioning yourself in a particular way so, for example, there are trees or water or sky behind your subject and not cars. You can then use natural elements in the background to add texture and pattern.
Rule number four is related to this: take three steps closer to your subject. Try to fill the picture with your subject rather than leaving a lot of air around—unless the background or surroundings are important.
And rule number five is to adjust your height to your subject. So, if they're much shorter, for example, a child, kneel or crouch down. The lens and their eyes should be at about the same level. You'll be amazed at the difference.
So those are the five rules. Let's look at another picture of the same person and see how the rules work in practice.

UNIT 10 RECORDING W10.4

1 It's well worth a visit
2 Let's head over to the
3 Supposedly, they had to interrupt
4 Believe it or not, it took
5 It was originally built as
6 Well, they were founded in
7 The story goes that he used

R5 RECORDING R5.1

1 rescue, touching, mugging
2 hype, height, gory
3 thought-provoking, now and then, groundbreaking
4 rave reviews, accuse, full of suspense
5 hacking, cause, fall for
6 hysterical, bribery, deceive

> **Catalogue Publication Data**
>
> Authors: Frances Eales, Steve Oakes, Louis Harrison
> *American Speakout Upper-Intermediate Workbook*
> First published
> Pearson Educación de México, S.A. de C.V., 2017
> ISBN: 978-607-32-4065-9
> Area: ELT
> Format: 21 x 29.7 cm   Page count: 88

Managing Director: Sergio Fonseca ■ **Innovation & Learning Delivery Director:** Alan David Palau ■ **Regional Content Manager - English:** Andrew Starling ■ **Publisher:** A. Leticia Alvarez ■ **Content Support:** Isabel Moreno ■ **Editorial Services Manager:** Asbel Ramírez ■ **Art and Design Coordinator:** Juan Manuel Santamaria ■ **Design Process Supervisor:** Aristeo Redondo ■ **Layout:** Sergio Guzmán ■ **Cover Design:** Ana Elena García ■ **Photo Research:** Beatriz Monsiváis ■ **Photo Credits:** Pearson Asset Library (PAL)

Contact: soporte@pearson.com
This adaptation is published by arrangement with Pearson Education Limited

Pearson Education Limited
Edinburgh Gate
Harlow
Essex CM20 2JE
England
and Associated Companies throughout the world.

© Pearson Education Limited 2015

Used by permission and adapted from
Speakout 2ND EDITION Upper-Intermediate Workbook
ISBN: 978-1-4479-7718-6
First published, 2015
All Rights Reserved.

Every effort has been made to trace the copyright holders and we apologize in advance for any unintentional omissions. We would be pleased to insert the appropriate acknowledgment in any subsequent edition of this publication.

Esta obra se terminó de imprimir el mes de enero de 2017 en los talleres de Editorial Progreso, S. A. de C. V., Naranjo Núm. 248, Colonia Santa María la Ribera, Delegación Cuauhtémoc, C. P. 06400, Ciudad de México

First published, 2017

ISBN PRINT BOOK: 978-607-32-4065-9

D.R. © 2017 por Pearson Educación de México, S.A. de C.V.
Avenida Antonio Dovalí Jaime #70
Torre B, Piso 6, Colonia Zedec Ed. Plaza Santa Fe
Delegación Álvaro Obregón, México, Ciudad de México, C. P. 01210

www.PearsonELT.com

Impreso en México. *Printed in Mexico.*

1 2 3 4 5 6 7 8 9 0 - 20 19 18 17

Pearson

All rights reserved. No part of this publication may be reproduced, stored in a retrieval system, or transmitted in any form or by any means, electronic, mechanical, photocopying, recording, or otherwise, without the prior permission of the publisher.

Pearson Hispanoamérica
Argentina ■ Belice ■ Bolivia ■ Chile ■ Colombia ■ Costa Rica ■ Cuba ■ República Dominicana ■ Ecuador ■ El Salvador ■ Guatemala ■ Honduras ■ México ■ Nicaragua ■ Panamá ■ Paraguay ■ Perú ■ Uruguay ■ Venezuela

Illustration acknowledgments
Illustrated by Eric@kja-artists

Photo acknowledgments
The publisher would like to thank the following for their kind permission to reproduce their photographs:

(Key: b-bottom; c-centre; l-left; r-right; t-top)

123RF.com: Raman Maisei 8b, Maridav 8c, 123RF.com 9bl, 9br, Natalia Lisovskaya 30b, 123RF.com 35, Wavebreak Media Ltd 48, 123RF.com 51 (tea), 51tl, 51tr, Nils Weymann 68t, 68b; **Alamy Images:** Cultura Creative 8t, PhotoAlto 23, Ashley Cooper 28, Natural Visions 50, Fotolia.com: MasterLu 69; **Getty Images:** Michael Blann 15, Trevor Williams 25, Domen Colja 29, Elie Bernager 47, John Lund/Sam Diephuis 61; **Press Association Images:** Tsvangirai Mukwazhi 21; **Shutterstock.com:** Jack.Q 24, Kavram 30t, Nikkos 38, Nejron Photo's 41, d13 44b, Kurhan 44t, PhotoBarmaley 51 (coffee), Diego Cervo 62; **The Kobal Collection:** Paramount 65.

All other images © Pearson Education

Every effort has been made to trace the copyright holders and we apologize in advance for any unintentional omissions. We would be pleased to insert the appropriate acknowledgment in any subsequent edition of this publication.